OXFORD
GCSE Maths
Higher PLUS
Homework

Clare Plass formerly of Trent College, Nottingham

About this book

This book has been written to provide extra exercises for the topics covered within the Higher Plus Student Book. There are four exercises for each Student Book unit: Homework 1 reviews previous topics, Homework 2 covers unit lessons 1 and 2, Homework 3 covers unit lessons 3 and 4 and Homework 4 covers unit lesson 5 as well as reviewing the rest of the unit with exam-style questions.

Contents

OXFORD
UNIVERSITY PRESS

OXFORD
UNIVERSITY PRESS

Great Clarendon Street, Oxford OX2 6DP

Oxford University Press is a department of the University of Oxford.
It furthers the University's objective of excellence in research, scholarship,
and education by publishing worldwide in

Oxford New York

Auckland   Cape Town   Dar es Salaam   Hong Kong   Karachi
Kuala Lumpur   Madrid   Melbourne   Mexico City   Nairobi
New Delhi   Shanghai   Taipei   Toronto

With offices in

Argentina   Austria   Brazil   Chile   Czech Republic   France   Greece
Guatemala   Hungary   Italy   Japan   South Korea   Poland   Portugal
Singapore   Switzerland   Thailand   Turkey   Ukraine   Vietnam

Oxford is a registered trade mark of Oxford University Press
in the UK and in certain other countries

British Library Cataloguing in Publication Data

Data available

ISBN 0-19-915081-8

ISBN 978-0-19-915081-6

10 9 8 7 6 5 4 3 2 1

Typeset by MCS Publishing Services Ltd., Salisbury, Wiltshire

Printed in Great Britain by Ashford Colour Press Ltd., Gosport

Front cover photo: Photodisc Green

1 Work out these, giving your answers in simplest form.

   a $\frac{7}{12}+\frac{1}{3}$ **b** $\frac{7}{9}-\frac{2}{5}$

   c $1\frac{3}{4}\times\frac{6}{7}$ **d** $\frac{x}{3}\div\frac{x}{5}$

2 Change each of these to a fraction.

   a $0.5\dot{3}\dot{4}$ **b** $0.0\dot{6}$

   c $2.2\dot{4}$ **d** $-1.\dot{9}\dot{8}$

3 Solve these equations:

   a $3x-19=11$ **b** $2(x+4)=6$

   c $4x+9=24-x$ **d** $6(2x+1)=3(x-7)$

   e $\frac{2}{3}x-5=7$ **f** $2(\frac{1}{4}x-3)=-x$

4 A game is played using a spinner with unequal sectors. The probability of obtaining each symbol is shown in the table below:

Star	0.25
Diamond	x
Heart	0.05
Circle	0.15
Triangle	0.1

a What is the probability of the spinner landing on a diamond?

b If the spinner is spun 100 times, how many times would you expect to land on a star?

1 Work out these, giving your answer as a power of 10.

   a $10^4 \times 10^8$ **b** $10^{12} \div 10^7$

   c $10^3 \div 10^9$ **d** $10^5 \times 10^4 \div 10^2$

   e $10^8 \div 10^4 \times 10^{-3}$ **f** $10^5 \div 10^{-4} \times 10^6$

   g $10^2 \times 10^2 \times 10^2 \times 10^2$ **h** $\dfrac{10^{-8} \times 10^3}{10^7 \times 10^{-9}}$

2 Write these numbers in standard form.

   a 600   **b** 19 340

   c 2 000 000   **d** 15

   e 17 504   **f** 718 300

3 Change these numbers in standard form to ordinary numbers.

   a 6.3×10^2 **b** 14.05×10^6

   c 1.934×10^3 **d** 7×10^5

   e 8.3×10^0 **f** 16.4×10^1

4 Work these out using a calculator, giving your answer in standard form.

   a $(2.4 \times 10^5) \times (1.92 \times 10^{-3})$

   b $(4.7 \times 10^8) \div (3.2 \times 10^3)$

   c $(1.26 \times 10^{-3}) \div (2.52 \times 10^{-4})$

   d $(6.39 \times 10^4) \div (3.6 \times 10^{-2})$

   e $(2.9 \times 10^6) \times (4.21 \times 10^{-2})$

   f $(1.96 \times 10^{-3}) \times (5.2 \times 10^7)$

1 Write these numbers in standard form.

   a 0.16   **b** 0.005 32

   c 0.060 01   **d** 0.04

   e 0.000 000 7   **f** 0.004 321

2 Change these numbers in standard form to ordinary numbers.

   a 4.8×10^{-2} **b** 6×10^{-5}

   c 2.003×10^{-3} **d** 2.9×10^{-1}

   e 8.999×10^{-8} **f** 1.717×10^{-10}

3 Work these out without using a calculator, giving your answer in standard form.

   a $(8 \times 10^{4}) \div (4 \times 10^{2})$

   b $(9.6 \times 10^{-8}) \div (3 \times 10^{-5})$

   c $(6 \times 10^{-4}) \times (5 \times 10^{9})$

   d $(2.4 \times 10^{3}) \times (5 \times 10^{4})$

   e $(3 \times 10^{5}) \div (6 \times 10^{-2})$

4 Write each of these numbers as a product of its prime factors.

   a 210   **b** 540

   c 1350   **d** 1750

   e 1694   **f** 4732

5 The area of a rectangular lawn is 90 m². By grouping the prime factors of 90, find all the possible dimensions of the lawn.

Hint: Remember to include the dimensions where one length is 1 m.

1 In 2004, the Duke of Westborough had an estimated fortune of £2600 million.

  a Express this number in standard form.
  b If the Duke decides to share his fortune equally amongst the 6×10^7 people in the United Kingdom work out how much each person receives, to the nearest penny.

2 The population of the Netherlands is approximately 16.4×10^6 people.

  a Write this number given in standard form as an ordinary number.

  The Netherlands has an area of approximately 41 000 km^2.
  b Write this number in standard form.
  c Work out the population density **without** using a calculator, giving your answer in standard form.

3 The distance from Earth to the Sun is approximately 1.44×10^8 km.

  a Change this number from standard form to an ordinary number.
  b If light travels at a speed of approximately 3×10^5 km/s, work out how long it takes for light to travel from Earth to the Sun.

4 a Express these numbers as products of their prime factors.

    i 750 **ii** 1470

  b By drawing an appropriate Venn diagram, find

    i the HCF and **ii** the LCM of 750 and 1470.

  c Find the smallest number that can be multiplied by 750 to give a square number.

1 Write each of these numbers as a product of its prime factors.

    a 720 **b** 84 **c** 910 **d** 36 **e** 256

2 By drawing an appropriate Venn diagram, find the **i** HCF and **ii** LCM of these pairs of numbers:

    a 36 and 84   **b** 256 and 720
    c 84 and 910   **d** 63 and 260

Hint: For parts **a** to **c** you have done the hard work in question 1!

3 Write each number in standard index form.

    a 2056   **b** 871 342   **c** 0.000 486
    d 25.8×10^4 **e** 0.36×10^{-3}

4 Work these out, without using a calculator, giving your answer in standard index form.

    a $(6 \times 10^9) \div (2 \times 10^3)$
    b $(3 \times 10^{-3}) \times (7 \times 10^4)$
    c $(8 \times 10^{14}) \div (2 \times 10^{-2})$
    d $(4 \times 10^7) \times (9 \times 10^3)$
    e $(3.2 \times 10^5) \div (4 \times 10^3)$

5 Find the circumference and area of each circle.

    a   **b**

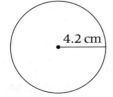
4.2 cm

5.8 cm

For all questions, give your answers to 1 decimal place.

1 Find the area of each sector.

a

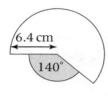

40° 16 mm

b

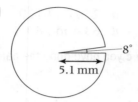

100° 9 cm

c

6.4 cm 140°

d

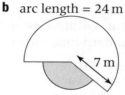

8° 5.1 mm

2 Find the perimeter of each of the sectors in question **1**.

3 Find each of the shaded angles.

a   arc length = 4.2 cm

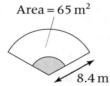

5 cm

b   arc length = 24 m

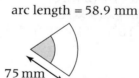

7 m

c   Area = 65 m²

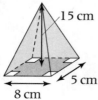

8.4 m

d   arc length = 58.9 mm

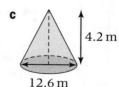

75 mm

4 Find the volume of each solid.

a

15 cm 5 cm 8 cm

b

60 mm 124 mm²

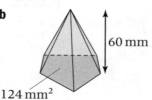

c

4.2 m 12.6 m

For all questions, give your answers to 3 significant figures.

1 Find the surface area of each solid.

    a Regular tetrahedron of side 4 cm

    b Square-based pyramid, base length = 10 cm, vertical height above mid-point of square base = 12 cm

2 Find the curved surface area of each cone.

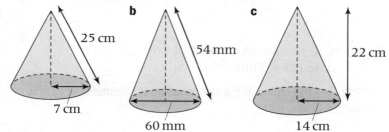

a 25 cm, 7 cm   **b** 54 mm, 60 mm   **c** 22 cm, 14 cm

Hint: Use the formula: Curved surface area of cone = $\pi r l$

3 Both of these sectors are folded to form cones. Find the curved surface area of each cone.

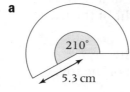

a 210°, 5.3 cm   **b** 110°, 4 m

4 The cuboid and cone have the same surface area. Find the radius of the base of the cone.

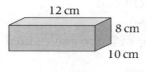

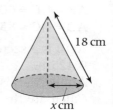

12 cm, 8 cm, 10 cm   18 cm, x cm

For all questions, give your answers to 1 decimal place.

1 Find **i** the volume and **ii** the surface area for each sphere.

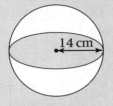
a   14 cm

b   2.8 cm

c   6.12 m

2 A sphere has a surface area of 100 cm². Calculate the volume of the sphere

Hint: Find the radius of the sphere using the formula:
Surface area = $4\pi r^2$

3 A child's toy consists of a cone attached to a hemisphere. The radius of the hemisphere is 3 cm and the total height of the toy is 7 cm. Find

   a the volume of the toy
   b the surface area of the toy.

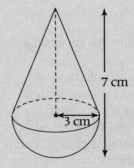
7 cm   3 cm

4 A wall mirror is shaped as follows:

ABCD is a rectangle where
AB = DC = 60 cm and
AD = BC = 85 cm.

AOB is a sector of a circle of radius 0.425m.
Angle AOB is 90°.
Calculate the perimeter of the mirror.

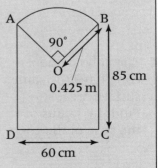
A   B   90°   O   0.425 m   85 cm   D   C   60 cm

1 If $x = 2 \times 10^5$ and $y = 1.6 \times 10^{-3}$ calculate these, giving your answers in standard form.

a xy **b** x^2 **c** $\dfrac{y}{x}$ **d** $\dfrac{x^3}{y}$

2 **a** Express 240 and 504 as the product of their prime factors.
   b Use your answer to part **a** to find out the HCF of 240 and 504.

3 The base and top face of a piece of cheese is a sector of a circle, centre O.
The angle AOB = 50°
The radius OB = 12 cm

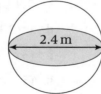

   a Calculate the area of the base of the cheese.
   b If the cheese is 4 cm thick, calculate the volume of the piece of cheese.

4 Find the surface area of these solids.

a

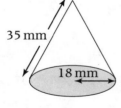

35 mm

18 mm

b

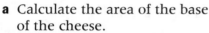

2.4 m

c

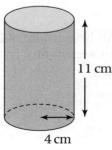

11 cm

4 cm

d

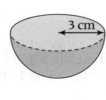

3 cm

1 Simplify these expressions.

a $x^2 \times x^5$ **b** $y^{-3} \div y^4$

c $\dfrac{t^2}{t^3}$ **d** $\dfrac{a^3 \times a^5}{a}$

e $(b^{-2})^4$ **f** $\dfrac{2x^3 \times 3x^6}{x^4}$

g $5p^3 \times 2p^2 q$ **h** $(4m^{-2})^3$

2 If $a = 3^2$ and $b = 3^5$ work these out, leaving your answer as an index number.

a ab **b** $\dfrac{a}{b}$ **c** a^2 **d** ab^2 **e** $(3b)^2$

3 Expand and simplify these expressions.

a $4(3x + 7)$ **b** $2y(4x - 1)$

c $6(2p + 1) - 4(p + 9)$ **d** $x^2(2 + x^3)$

e $(x + 3)(x + 9)$ **f** $(3x + 4)(x - 5)$

g $(2t - 9)^2$ **h** $(3 - m)(m + 4) + (2m - 1)^2$

4 Given that two consecutive numbers can be written as $2n$ and $2n + 1$, prove that the sum of the squares of any two consecutive numbers is an odd number.

1 Factorise these by removing common factors.

a $6p + 3$

b $12x - 15$

c $3xy + 2x$

d $4y^2 + 12y^3 + xy$

e $2pq^2 + 5p^2q$

f $6a^3b - 3a^2 + 12$

g $2(x + y) - (x + y)^2$

h $wx + wy - 3x - 3y$

2 Factorise each of these fully.

a $x^2 + 6x + 5$

b $x^2 + 7x - 18$

c $x^2 - 3x - 18$

d $x^2 - 15x - 100$

e $x^2 - 21x + 110$

f $x^2 - 16x + 64$

g $3x^2 + 21x + 30$

h $x^3 - 6x^2 - 40x$

Hint: You may have to use double brackets and common factors.

3 Factorise each of these using double brackets.

a $2x^2 + 11x + 5$

b $3x^2 + 11x + 6$

c $5x^2 + 6x - 8$

d $6x^2 + 11x + 3$

e $12x^2 - 23x + 5$

f $15x^2 + 34x + 15$

4 Copy and complete each of these.

a $\square - 7x - x^2 = (2 \square x)(x + 9)$

b $15 + \square - 2x^2 = (\square - x)(2x + 5)$

c $19x - 10 - \square = (5 - 2x)(3x - \square)$

1 Factorise

  a $x^2 - 64$ **b** $m^2 - 25$

  c $49 - t^2$ **d** $a^2 - b^2$

  e $9y^2 - 100$ **f** $x^2 - \frac{1}{9}$

  g $25a^2 - \frac{4}{9}$ **h** $2a^3 - 32a$

2 a Simplify

    i $\dfrac{p^3}{p^4}$ **ii** $\dfrac{2q^2 \times 5q^5}{q^4}$

  b Expand and simplify
    i $(3x + 4)(x - 5)$
    ii $(3x - y)^2$

3 The area of this trapezium is 525 m^2.

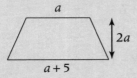

  a Show that $2a^2 + 5a - 525 = 0$.
  b Factorise the left hand side of $2a^2 + 5a - 525 = 0$.

4 $a = 3^x$ and $b = 3^y$.
  Express in terms of a and/or b

  a 3^{x+y} **b** 3^{2x} **c** 3^{y-1}

1 The United States of America covers an area of approximately 3 800 000 square miles.

a Write this as a number in standard form.

It is known that approximately 2.6×10^5 square miles of the area of the United States is water.

b Write this number as an ordinary number.

c Using your calculator input these numbers in standard form and work out the percentage of the United States that is water.

Hint: To put 5.3×10^7 into a Casio calculator type 5.3 EXP 7

2 Expand and simplify

a $5(3 - 4x)$ **b** $6a\,(2a + 3b)$
c $y^2(y + x)$ **d** $(x + 3)(x + 7)$
e $(2t - 3)(t + 5)$ **f** $(p + 7)^2 + 2(p - 3)$

3 Find the volume of this solid.

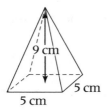

4 Work out these missing angles.

a

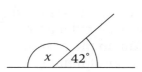

b

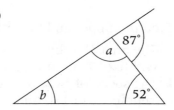

1 Round these numbers to the degree of accuracy given in brackets.

    a 1451 (nearest 100)   **b** 294 (nearest 10)

    c 23.56 (nearest whole)   **d** 34.89 (1 decimal place)

    e 2104 (nearest 1000)   **f** 12.698 (2 decimal places)

    g 0.584 72 (3 decimal places)   **h** 1.99 (1 decimal place)

2 Round these numbers to the degree of accuracy given in brackets.

    a 1.347 (3 significant figures)

    b 12.831 (3 significant figures)

    c 0.004 53 (2 significant figures)

    d 0.3004 (2 significant figures)

    e 1239 (2 significant figures)

    f 63 920 (1 significant figure)

    g 235.95 (4 significant figures)

    h 10 957 (3 significant figures)

3 Write the upper and lower bounds for these measurements to the degree of accuracy given.

    a 4 m (nearest unit)

    b 650 mm (nearest 10)

    c 241.3 g (1 decimal place)

    d 45 ml (nearest 5 ml)

    e 8300 km (2 significant figures)

    f 11.53 secs (2 decimal places)

4 Find the upper and lower bounds of these calculations.

    a The area of a sheet of paper with length 29.4 cm and width 20.7 cm, measured to the nearest millimetre.

    b The speed of a car travelling 164 km, to the nearest kilometre, in 120 minutes, to the nearest minute.

1 By copying and completing this table, state whether a positive number will give a result that is *larger, smaller* or *the same size*.

	The result is larger, smaller or the same size?
×1.7	*larger*
÷0.5	
×0.9	
÷1.25	
×1	

2 True or False?

a Dividing by 0.2 is the same as multiplying by 5.
Show your working.

b Multiplying by 0.25 is the same as dividing by 4.
Show your working.

Hint: Use fractions to demonstrate.

3 Work these out using mental methods.

a 5×0.4 **b** 0.03×0.5
c $6 \div 0.2$ **d** $0.8 \div 0.04$
e 0.12×0.6 **f** $1.8 \div 0.03$
g 1.5×0.15 **h** $2.24 \div 1.6$

4 Work these out using mental methods.

a 10% of 155   **b** 50% of 284   **c** 20% of 135
d 30% of 75   **e** 25% of 42   **f** 15% of 120
g 8% of 25   **h** 17.5% of 16

Hint: Find 10% by dividing the number by 10 and 1% by dividing the number by 100.

5 Work these out using mental methods.

a $\frac{1}{8}$ of 192   **b** $\frac{3}{8}$ of 256   **c** $\frac{1}{2} \times \frac{1}{4}$ **d** $\frac{4}{7} + 1\frac{1}{3}$ **e** $\frac{4}{9} \div \frac{2}{3}$

1 Work these out using pencil and paper methods.

a $\frac{1}{2} + \frac{3}{4}$ **b** $1\frac{1}{3} - \frac{2}{7}$

c $4 \times \frac{3}{5}$ **d** $2\frac{3}{4} \div 2\frac{1}{4}$

e 4.52×7.9 **f** $13.5 \div 0.75$

g $436.8 + 19.56$ **h** 32.5% of 140

i 28% of 225 **j** 129 as a percentage of 64

2 a Use approximations to estimate the value of

$$\frac{458 \times 0.036}{1.69}$$

Show all of your working.

b Use your calculator to find the exact answer.

c Calculate the percentage error for the approximation.

Hint: Round each number to 1 significant figure.

3 Rupert decides to send a red rose to his girlfriend. The rose measures 30 cm, to the nearest centimetre. Rupert buys a presentation box of length 30.1 cm, measured to the nearest millimetre.

a Explain why the rose may not fit inside the box.

b What is the maximum length that Rupert may have to cut from the stem of the rose in order to make it fit in the box?

4 Using the fact that

$$56 \times 421 = 23\,576$$

write the answer to these calculations.

a 5.6×42.1

b $0.56 \times 421\,000$

c $23.576 \div 5.6$

1 These calculations all involve the number 8. State whether the answer to each question will be smaller or larger than 8. You do not have to work out the answers.

 a 8×0.4　**b** 8×1.3　**c** $8 \div 1.5$　**d** $8 \div 0.2$

2 Round these numbers to the degree of accuracy given in brackets.

 a 4.329 (2 decimal places)
 b 3.825 (2 significant figures)
 c 0.215 63 (3 decimal places)
 d 0.001 85 (1 significant figure)
 e 10 214 (3 significant figures)
 f 1.200 45 (4 significant figures)
 g 1.995 (2 decimal places)
 h 45 126 (2 significant figures)

3 Factorise each expression.

 a $4ab - 2a$　　　　**b** $10x^2 - 15x$
 c $a^3 b^2 c + 3a^2 c$　　**d** $3p^2 + 9p^3 + pq$
 e $ax + ay - 5x - 5y$　**f** $x^2 + 8x + 15$
 g $x^2 + 5x - 6$　　　**h** $3x^2 - 10x - 8$

4 Find the volume of this cylinder. Give your answer to 3 significant figures.

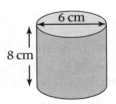

5 Find the surface area of this hemisphere. Give your answer to 3 significant figures.

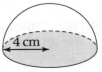

Hint: The surface area of a sphere is $4\pi r^2$ so halve this. Don't forget the base of the object – what shape is it?

1 Solve these equations with algebraic terms on one side.

    a $3x + 7 = 25$ **b** $2(4y - 1) = 18$

    c $5(6 - 4x) = 25$ **d** $3p^2 + 5 = 32$

    e $19 = 17 - 2x$ **f** $22 = 4(5y - 2)$

    g $2 + 6x - 3 - 3x = 0$ **h** $4m^3 - 9 = 23$

2 Solve these equations with algebraic terms on both sides.

    a $7x + 5 = 3x - 7$ **b** $2x - 10 = 7x - 11$

    c $9 - p = 4p - 11$ **d** $3(y - 8) = 4(2y + 9)$

    e $2(3 - x) = 5(4x - 1)$ **f** $14m - (2m + 8) = 1$

    g $4(y + 8) - 3(y + 5) = 3(y + 1)$ **h** $6(x - 2) = 9x - 3(2x - 1)$

3 Solve these equations involving fractions.

    a $\dfrac{x + 9}{3} = \dfrac{2(x + 1)}{4}$ **b** $\dfrac{6p}{5} = \dfrac{8p - 4}{3}$

    c $\dfrac{y}{3} + \dfrac{2y}{5} = 11$ **d** $\dfrac{m}{3} + \dfrac{1}{4} = \dfrac{m}{4}$

4 If I add together one third of my age and one ninth of my age I get 8. If my age is x, form an equation in x and solve to find the value of my age.

5 In 4 years time Clare will be twice the age she was 10 years ago. Use an algebraic approach to determine Clare's age.

A2 HW3 Algebraic fractions

1 Simplify these fractions fully and find the odd one out.

$$\frac{18x}{6}$$ $$\frac{15x^2}{5x}$$ $$\frac{6abx}{2ab}$$ $$\frac{4x-12x^2}{4x}$$ $$\frac{6x^2+3x}{2x+1}$$

2 Simplify these fractions fully.

a $\dfrac{x+1}{x^2+3x+2}$ **b** $\dfrac{x^2+4x-21}{x-3}$ **c** $\dfrac{x-2}{x^2-4}$

d $\dfrac{x^2-3x-18}{x^2-10x+24}$ **e** $\dfrac{x^2-8x}{x^2-3x-40}$

3 Simplify these fractional multiplications and divisions.

a $\dfrac{2x}{3}\times\dfrac{3}{4}$ **b** $\dfrac{8xy}{9}\times\dfrac{3}{y}$ **c** $\dfrac{x}{5}\div\dfrac{x}{3}$

d $\dfrac{x+1}{4}\times\dfrac{3}{x^2+6x+5}$ **e** $\dfrac{x^2-9}{12}\div\dfrac{x^2+x-12}{6}$

4 Simplify each of these.

a $\dfrac{2a}{5}+\dfrac{a}{5}$ **b** $\dfrac{2x}{3}+\dfrac{x}{6}$ **c** $\dfrac{3}{p}-\dfrac{4}{q}$

d $\dfrac{x+3}{4}+\dfrac{x+7}{4}$ **e** $\dfrac{2x+1}{5}-\dfrac{3x+2}{3}$ **f** $\dfrac{4}{a+2}-\dfrac{3}{a-3}$

5 A rectangle has length $=\dfrac{3a^2-5a-2}{12}$ and width $=\dfrac{4}{3a+1}$.

Its area is 1 cm². Find the dimensions of the rectangle.

1 Solve the equation

$$x - \frac{5}{x} = 4$$

Hint: There are two solutions.

2 Solve the equation

$$\frac{3(x-4)}{x^2-16} + \frac{2}{x-1} = \frac{5}{6}$$

Hint: First factorise $x^2 - 16$ and then cancel.

3 If $\dfrac{3}{x+2} + 2 = \dfrac{9}{2x+1}$

a Show that $4x^2 + 7x - 11 = 0$.
b Find the two solutions to the equation.

4 These trapezia have the same area.
Find their dimensions.

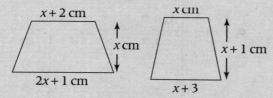

1 a Work these out using mental methods.

    i $\frac{3}{8}$ of 96   **ii** 15% of 240

    iii $\frac{3}{7}$ of 105   **iv** 45% of 160

  b Write these fractions as percentages, using mental methods.

    i $\frac{19}{25}$ **ii** $\frac{17}{20}$ **iii** $\frac{127}{200}$ **iv** $\frac{23}{40}$

Hint: Find a fraction equivalent to each of these fractions with a denominator of 100.

2 Solve these double-sided equations.

  a $4(x + 3) = 7x - 6$

  b $5(a - 4) = 2(a + 2)$

  c $5(t + 1) = 3(3t - 1)$

  d $5(3 - p) = 3(4 - p)$

  e $7y - 2(y - 5) = 20$

  f $(m + 4)(m - 1) = (m + 1)^2$

3 a Find the area of this sector.   **b** Calculate the missing angle.

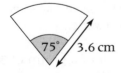

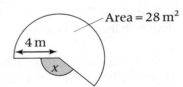

4 Find the surface area of a regular tetrahedron of side 6 cm.

Hint: Each face is an equilateral triangle of side 6 cm. Find the perpendicular height of each face using Pythagoras' theorem and use this to find the area of one face.

1 For each survey, suggest reasons why the chosen sample may be biased.

  a To find out the most popular sport amongst young people by asking teenage boys as they leave a football training academy.

  b To find out the most popular make of car by noting down the cars belonging to people who live on one road in Nottingham.

  c To find out the popularity of school uniforms by telephoning all the households on one page of the telephone directory on a Monday.

  d To find out the preferred choice of music for a school disco by asking the students who leave one of these discos at the end of the night.

2 A machine in a factory produces bottles with screw caps. Every 20th bottle is produced with a cap that does not seal the bottle. A factory worker notices one faulty bottle cap and decides to take a systematic sample of bottles in order to assess the scale of the problem. Explain the effect of sampling

  a every 20th bottle, beginning at bottle number 20

  b every 5th bottle, beginning at bottle number 5

  c every 5th bottle, beginning at bottle number 3.

Hint: Work out the proportion of faulty bottles in the sample taken and decide on the most likely conclusion of the factory worker.

3 Below is a list of the number of times each of a group of 30 students has visited the school library in the last term.

0	5	8	2	4	4	9	10	0	1
2	9	5	1	6	3	1	1	0	5
12	3	8	1	4	8	2	4	3	2

Using the random number generator on a calculator, choose a sample of eight of the answers given.

Hint: Assign a two-digit number to each of the answers above (0 is number 01, 5 is number 02, etc.). Press Ran# on your calculator.

1 Lorna is carrying out a survey in order to establish the popularity of school uniforms at her school. This table shows information about the gender and year group of the students.

	Male	Female
Year 7	100	115
Year 8	108	92
Year 9	88	122
Year 10	83	97
Year 11	124	71

  a She decides to choose a stratified sample of 50 students by gender and year group. Work out the numbers of students to be sampled.

  b Explain how to choose the male students from year 7.

2 A cattery receives a delivery of 500 pouches of a new brand of cat food: 225 pouches of chicken in jelly, 150 pouches of turkey in gravy and 125 pouches of tuna. Explain how the owners of the cattery could take a stratified sample of 30 pouches in order to test the quality of the cat food.

3 The table below shows the number of letters in the first 50 words of the novel *The Hobbit* by J. R. R. Tolkien.

Word length	1	2	3	4	5	6	7
Frequency	5	11	12	10	7	4	1

  a Find the **i** mean **ii** median **iii** mode.
  b Calculate the range.

4 Two dice are thrown and the smaller number of the two shown on the dice is subtracted from the larger. The results of 100 throws are shown in the table.

Result	0	1	2	3	4	5
Frequency	18	26	21	14	14	7

  a Calculate the median.
  b Calculate the interquartile range.

1 Annabel recorded her test results in the back of her exercise book.

Maths	English	Physics	Chemistry	Biology
88%	85%	77%	79%	▓▓

'My mean mark in these five tests was 81%.'
Unfortunately, Annabel noticed that there was an ink blot obscuring her mark in Biology. Can you help her to work out her Biology result?

2 There are 25 students in a class, 10 girls and 15 boys. On one particular night, the mean time spent on homework by the boys was 1.6 hours and the mean time spent on homework by the girls was 2.1 hours. Work out the mean time spent on homework by all the students in this class. Give your answer in hours and minutes.

3 There are g girls and b boys in a class. The mean number of minutes spent travelling to school for the girls is 15.25 and the mean number of minutes spent travelling to school for the boys is 18.5. Write an expression for the total amount of time spent travelling to school by this class.

4 The table shows the number of boys and girls in years 12 and 13 of a school.

	Year 12	Year 13
Boys	80	55
Girls	70	75

A teacher wants to find out whether or not to run a ski trip this year and decides to take a stratified sample of 50 pupils. Calculate the numbers of students to be sampled.

1 Value Added Tax (VAT) is 17.5%. In some discount stores, prices are given before VAT has been added. To find 17.5% of a number without using a calculator find

- 10% by dividing the number by 10
- 5% by halving the value of 10%
- 2.5% by halving the value of 5%

Then sum together the values.
Work out 17.5% of these prices, rounding to the nearest penny.

  a £120   **b** £80
  c £36   **d** £14
  e £25   **f** £6.50

2 Solve these equations with algebraic expressions in the denominator.

  a $\dfrac{5}{x+3} = \dfrac{9}{4x+1}$ **b** $\dfrac{3}{4x} = \dfrac{6}{3x-5}$

3 A metal sphere of radius 8 cm is to be melted down to make 10 smaller spheres of equal volume.
Find the radius of a small sphere.

Hint: Find the volume of the large sphere using $V = \frac{4}{3}\pi r^3$ and divide by 10. Use the formula again to find r.

4 The table shows the number of tea bags in 100 boxes marked 'average contents 80 tea bags'. Does the claim appear to be correct if the mean average is considered?

No. of bags	77	78	79	80	81	82	83
Frequency	5	12	23	32	18	9	1

Do not use a calculator for this exercise.

1 Work these out, simplifying where possible.

  a $\frac{3}{7} + \frac{1}{7}$ **b** $\frac{4}{9} + \frac{7}{9}$ **c** $\frac{5}{8} - \frac{1}{4}$ **d** $\frac{1}{2} + \frac{3}{4}$

  e $\frac{7}{12} - \frac{1}{3}$ **f** $\frac{3}{5} - \frac{1}{4}$ **g** $1\frac{1}{3} - \frac{2}{7}$ **h** $3\frac{1}{4} + 2\frac{5}{8}$

2 Work these out, simplifying where possible.

  a $4 \times \frac{3}{5}$ **b** $\frac{5}{8} \div 10$ **c** $\frac{1}{4} \times \frac{1}{3}$ **d** $\frac{2}{3} \div \frac{1}{4}$

  e $\frac{5}{12} \times \frac{3}{5}$ **f** $\frac{6}{7} \times \frac{14}{15}$ **g** $1\frac{1}{2} \div \frac{3}{8}$ **h** $2\frac{3}{4} \div 2\frac{1}{4}$

3 Work out one half of three-quarters of 168.
Show your working.

4 Jasmine drives $14\frac{1}{2}$ km to collect a friend and then travels
another $5\frac{3}{8}$ km in order to reach her workplace.

  a How many kilometres does Jasmine travel to work?

Jasmine and her friend always listen to the radio for the
portion of the journey that they are both in the car.

  b For what fraction of Jasmine's journey does she listen to
the radio?

5 Pair these cards together if they show equivalent numbers.
Which is the odd card out?

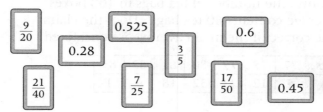

1 Pair these cards together if they show equivalent decimal numbers and percentages. Which is the odd card out?

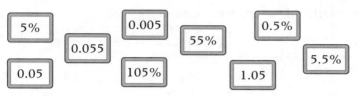

2 True or False?
To work out 109% of a number, multiply by 1.09.
Show your working.

Hint: Use fractions.

3 Arrange these fractions in ascending order.

a $\frac{1}{10}, \frac{2}{5}, \frac{1}{4}, \frac{1}{20}, \frac{3}{4}$ **b** $\frac{14}{15}, \frac{2}{3}, \frac{2}{5}, \frac{1}{10}, \frac{1}{6}$

c $\frac{5}{12}, \frac{1}{8}, \frac{1}{6}, \frac{2}{3}, \frac{7}{24}$ **d** $\frac{1}{2}, \frac{2}{5}, \frac{1}{30}, \frac{1}{12}, \frac{7}{15}$

4 Write these fractions, decimals and percentages in descending order.

a 50%, 0.42, 0.07, $\frac{7}{20}$, $\frac{2}{5}$, 12%, 0.9, $\frac{71}{100}$

b 0.7, 28%, 0.09, $\frac{1}{25}$, 37%, 1, 82%, $\frac{11}{20}$

5 Convert $0.\dot{9}$ to a fraction.
What integer is equivalent to this fraction?

Do not use a calculator in this exercise.

1 Two lengths of piping are fastened together.

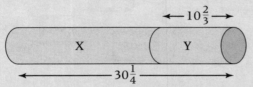

The combined length of the piping is $30\frac{1}{4}$ inches.
The length of piping marked Y is $10\frac{2}{3}$ inches.
Work out the length of the piping marked X.

2 Zac bought a van for £15 000.
Each year the van depreciated by 5%.
Work out the value of Zac's van 2 years after he
purchased it.

3 Sam buys a new jacket from his favourite shop.
The shop offers Sam a 20% discount as a loyalty reward.
Sam accepts the discount and pays £64 for the jacket.
What was the price of the jacket *before* the discount was
applied?

4 a Work out $3\frac{3}{5} \times 2\frac{2}{9}$.

   b Work out $4\frac{2}{3} \div 1\frac{2}{5}$.

1 Find the upper and lower bounds of these calculations.

a The area of a rectangular pond with length 4 m and width 3 m, measured to the nearest centimetre.

b The range of temperature during one day in Derby if the maximum recorded temperature was 28 °C and the minimum recorded temperature was 18 °C, to the nearest degree Celsius.

c The density of a piece of metal if its mass is 1125 g, to the nearest gram and its volume is 150 cm^3, to the nearest cubic centimetre.

2 Solve these inequalities.

a $2x - 5 > 17$ **b** $3(x + 1) \leqslant 2x$

c $1 + n \geqslant -3$ **d** $3 - 2x \leqslant 9$

e $\dfrac{x}{5} \geqslant 7$ **f** $\dfrac{2x}{3} - 1 < 5$

g $24 < 8x < 3x + 20$ **h** $x^2 \leqslant 64$

3 Calculate the volume of a cone of diameter 14 mm and slant height 25 mm. Give your answer to 3 significant figures.

Hint: Use Pythagoras' theorem to calculate the vertical height of the cone. Remember to halve the diameter! The volume of a cone is given by $V = \frac{1}{3}\pi r^2 h$.

4 Michael lists the number of students in each year group at his secondary school.

Year group	7	8	9	10	11
No. of students	240	248	235	252	225

He decides to take a stratified sample of 50 students. How many students from each year group should he choose?

1 Work out the missing angles, giving reasons for your answers.

a

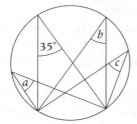

b

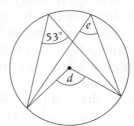

c

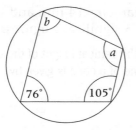

d

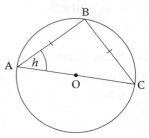

2 Work out the missing angles, giving reasons for your answers.

a

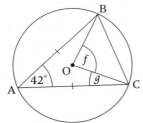

b

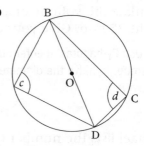

c

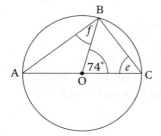

d

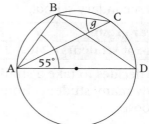

1 Work out the missing angles, giving reasons for your answers.

a
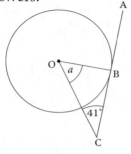

b
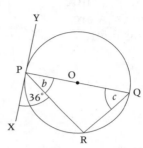

c
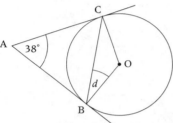

d
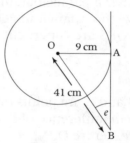

2 Work out the missing angles, giving reasons for your answers.

a
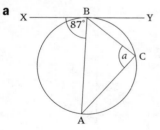

b
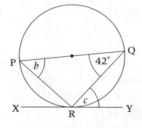

c
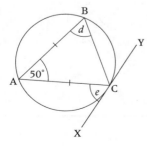

d
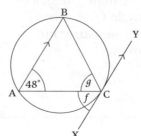

31

1 Prove that triangles OBA and OCA are congruent.

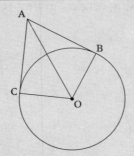

2 PQRS is a parallelogram. Prove that triangles SPQ and QRS are congruent.

3 A, B and C are points on the circumference of a circle, centre O.

   a Find angle AOC.
   b Give a reason for your answer.

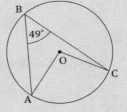

4 **a** Calculate the size of angle PRQ. Give reasons for your answer.
   b Calculate the size of angle QPR. Give reasons for your answer.

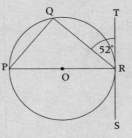

1 Mike wants to invest £200 for five years. His bank offers him two options:

Option 1 is simple interest of 5.25% per annum.

Option 2 is compound interest of 5% per annum.

Which option should Mike choose in order to achieve the most interest on his investment? Show all your working.

2 If I add together one quarter of my age and one sixteenth of my age I get 10. If my age is x, form an equation in x and solve to find the value of my age.

3 Solve these equations involving fractions.

a $\dfrac{x+4}{2} = \dfrac{3(x+6)}{5}$ **b** $\dfrac{2x}{5} = \dfrac{4(x-1)}{9}$

4 Find the missing angles.

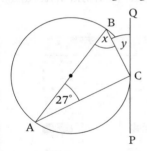

Hint: Look at the line AB. What sort of a line is it? This should help you find the angle ACB in order to proceed.

5 Charlotte carries out a survey to find out whether or not people belong to a gym. She asks all the people at her hockey club.

  a Write down two reasons as to why this is not a good way to find out whether or not people belong to a gym.

  b Devise a question that Charlotte could ask in order to find out how often people use a gym.

1 Generate the first five terms of each of these sequences and comment on the behaviour of each.

a $T_n = 5n - 3$ **b** $T_n = n(n + 1)$ **c** $T_n = 1 + \dfrac{1}{n}$

d $T_n = n^2 + 5n + 4$ **e** $T_n = (-2)^{n-1}$

Hint: Use the words diverge, converge, limit and oscillate.

2 Find the value of *n* that generates the term given from each of these sequences.

a $T_n = 6n - 1$; $T_n = 59$ **b** $T_n = (n - 1)^2$; $T_n = 49$
c $T_n = 5(n + 1)$; $T_n = 75$ **d** $T_n = n^3 + 4$; $T_n = 68$

Hint: Form an equation by letting the *n*th term and the term itself equal one another.

3 By drawing arrows, match each *n*th term formula with a pictorial sequence.

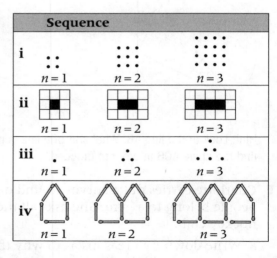

*n*th term
a $T = \dfrac{n(n+1)}{2}$
b $T = (n+1)^2$
c $T = 4n + 1$
d $T = 2(n + 3)$

4 Find the *n*th term of these linear sequences.

a 6, 11, 16, 21, 26, ...   **b** 20, 17, 14, 11, 8, ...
c $\dfrac{1}{4}, \dfrac{2}{9}, \dfrac{3}{16}, \dfrac{4}{25}, \dfrac{5}{36}, \ldots$ **d** −2, 4, −8, 16, −32

1 Find the nth term formula for each of these quadratic sequences.

  a 8, 15, 24, 35, 48, ...   **b** 9, 16, 25, 36, 49, ...
  c −1, 8, 23, 44, 71, ...   **d** 48, 42, 32, 18, 0, ...
  e $\frac{1}{4}$, 1, $2\frac{1}{4}$, 4, $6\frac{1}{4}$, ...

2 Generate a sequence to relate the number of tiles (T) with the height of each diagram (h).

3 Solve these quadratic equations.

  a $x^2 + 7x = 0$ **b** $x^2 + 9x + 18 = 0$
  c $2a^2 - 8a = 0$ **d** $p^2 + 5p - 36 = 0$
  e $x^2 - 5x - 14 = 0$ **f** $x^2 - 25 = 0$
  g $t^2 - 6t + 9 = 0$ **h** $5x^2 = 125$
  i $2m^2 = 5m + 12$ **j** $y(3y + 10) = 8$

4 Solve these equations.

  a $10x(x + 2) = 3(3x + 2)$ **b** $\dfrac{10}{x^2} + \dfrac{3}{x} = 1$

5 Molly's garden is 4 m longer than it is wide. The area of the garden is 21 m^2.

  a Show that if x is the length of the garden, $x^2 - 4x - 21 = 0$.
  b Find the two solutions to $x^2 - 4x - 21 = 0$. Explain why only one of them is the length of the garden.

1 Solve these quadratic equations using the quadratic equation formula, giving your answers to 3 significant figures.

   a $x^2 + 5x + 1 = 0$ **b** $2a^2 - 4a + 1 = 0$
   c $3x^2 + 7x - 2 = 0$ **d** $3p^2 = 6p + 2$
   e $3x - 7x^2 + 5 = 0$ **f** $5t^2 + 3 = 9t$

2 Solve these equations, giving your answers to 3 significant figures.

   a $x + \dfrac{2}{x} = 7$ **b** $x - \dfrac{3}{x} = 5$ **c** $\dfrac{2}{x+3} + \dfrac{1}{2x+1} = 4$

3 Jack is five years older than his wife, Florence.
   The product of their ages is 1050.
   Let Jack's age be x. Form an equation in x and solve to find how old Jack and Florence are.

4 The hypotenuse of a right-angled triangle is 4 mm longer than one side of the triangle and 1 mm longer than the other.

   a If the hypotenuse is x, write down the other two sides in terms of x.
   b Using Pythagoras' theorem, form an equation in x.
   c Solve the equation to find the three missing sides.

   Hint: The lengths of the sides are not whole numbers. Use the quadratic equation formula.

1 Write these fractions, decimals and percentages in ascending order.

  a $\frac{4}{7}$, 0.23, 16%, 11%, 0.05, $\frac{11}{16}$, 25%, $\frac{2}{9}$

  b 0.75, $\frac{1}{13}$, 18%, $\frac{4}{5}$, 28%, 0.03, $\frac{4}{15}$, 0.4

2 Solve these quadratic equations using the quadratic equation formula, giving your answers to 3 significant figures.

  a $x^2 + 8x + 3 = 0$
  b $3a^2 - 6a - 1 = 0$
  c $2t^2 = 5t - 1$
  d $4t^2 + 2 = 7t$

3 **a** Calculate the size of angle x. Give reasons for your answer.
  b Calculate the size of angle y. Give reasons for your answer.

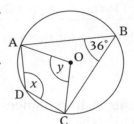

4 Five coins are tossed and the number of heads is recorded each time. The results of 200 tosses are shown in the table below.

Number of heads	0	1	2	3	4	5
Frequency	8	30	58	62	34	8

  a Calculate the median.
  b Calculate the interquartile range.

1 Elsie recorded the height, in centimetres, of each of the eleven sunflowers in her garden. She put the heights in order.

130 132 134 138 140 140 142 146 148 150 152

a Find
  i the lower quartile
  ii the upper quartile.
b Draw a box plot for these data.

2 Harry summarised the heights of the large number of 'Queen Elizabeth' rose bushes planted in his garden.

Smallest: 94 cm	Lower Quartile: 106 cm	Median: 118 cm
Tallest: 135 cm	Upper Quartile: 124 cm	

Draw a box plot for the data.

3 The heights, h, in centimetres, of 120 'Peace' rose bushes are given in the table.

Height, h cm	Frequency
$110 < h \leqslant 115$	32
$115 < h \leqslant 120$	44
$120 < h \leqslant 125$	22
$125 < h \leqslant 130$	13
$130 < h \leqslant 135$	8
$135 < h \leqslant 140$	1

a Draw a cumulative frequency table for the data.
b Draw a cumulative frequency diagram for the data.

1 The table gives information concerning the examination results of a group of 100 students.

a Draw a cumulative frequency table and diagram for these data.

b Estimate
  i the median
  ii the interquartile range from the graph.

c Estimate the number of students that passed the examination if the pass mark was 55%.

Test result, t%	Frequency
$40 < t \leqslant 50$	5
$50 < t \leqslant 60$	20
$60 < t \leqslant 70$	34
$70 < t \leqslant 80$	27
$80 < t \leqslant 90$	12
$90 < t \leqslant 100$	2

2 The table gives information concerning the lifetime in hours, h, of 120 light bulbs.

a Draw a cumulative frequency table and diagram for these data.

b Use the graph to estimate

  i the number of light bulbs with a lifetime of 975 hours or less

  ii the number of light bulbs with a lifetime of more than 1075 hours.

Hours, h	Frequency
$900 < h \leqslant 950$	6
$950 < h \leqslant 1000$	18
$1000 < h \leqslant 1050$	40
$1050 < h \leqslant 1100$	28
$1100 < h \leqslant 1150$	16
$1150 < h \leqslant 1200$	12

c Find
  i the median
  ii the lower and upper quartiles.

d Use your results to draw a box and whisker diagram.

Hint: Use lower bound of first class and upper bound of last class to estimate the minimum and maximum as they are not given.

1 The graph shows the waiting times for two MOT 'sit and wait' test centres.

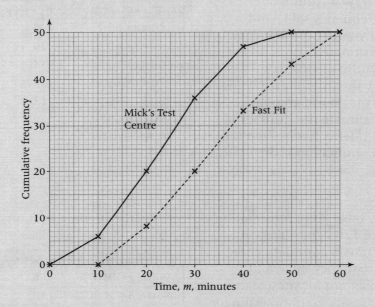

a Write down three comparisons concerning the waiting times at 'Mick's Test Centre' and 'Fast Fit'.

b Use the graphs above to find

   i the median for each of the two test centres.

   ii the lower and upper quartiles for each of the two test centres.

c Use your results to draw two box and whisker diagrams.

1 **a** Write 150 and 735 as products of their prime factors.
 b Find **i** the HCF **ii** the LCM of 150 and 735.

 Hint: Use factor trees to help you.

2 Generate the first five terms of these sequences and comment on the behaviour of each.

 a $T_n = 2^n + 1$ **b** $T_n = \dfrac{1}{n(n+1)}$ **c** $T_n = n^2 + 3n + 2$

 d $T_n = 10 - n$ **e** $T_n = 1 + 3(-1)^{n+1}$

 Hint: Use the words diverge, converge, limit and oscillate.

3 Factorise these equations.

 a $x^2 - 9$ **b** $p^2 - 49$ **c** $4n^2 - 81$
 d $x^2 - \dfrac{4}{25}$ **e** $3a^3 - 12a$

4 Ashim draws this picture on a piece of paper measuring 12 cm by 8 cm. He colours the six circles red and the rest of the paper blue.

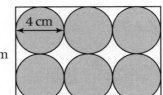

Calculate the area of the paper that is blue.

5 There are 14 girls and 10 boys in a class of students. The average number of DVDs owned by the girls is g and the average number of DVDs owned by the boys is b. Write an expression for the average number of DVDs owned by the whole class.

1 Which of these lines passes through the point (2, 3)?

Line	✓ or ✗
$y = x + 1$	
$3y = 2x + 1$	
$2y = x + 4$	
$y = 4x - 5$	
$y = 5 - 2x$	

2 Which of these lines is parallel to the line $y = 2x + 3$?

Line	✓ or ✗
$y = 3x + 2$	
$y = 2x - 1$	
$2y = x - 3$	
$2y = 4x + 3$	
$3y - 2 = 6x$	

3 Find the gradient of
  a AB
  b BC
  c DC
  d AD.

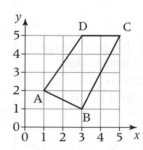

4 Sketch each of these line graphs on a separate set of axes.

  a $y = 3x + 2$　　　**b** $2y = x + 4$　　　**c** $y = 5 - x$

5 Find the equation of a line which is parallel to $y = 3x + 6$ and passes through

  a (0, −2)　　　**b** (2, 5)　　　**c** (4, 1)

1 a Find the equation of a line that is parallel to the line
  i $y = 4 - 2x$ **ii** $2y = x + 6$ **iii** $y = \frac{1}{3}x + 4$

 b Find the equation of a line that is perpendicular to each of the lines in part **a**.

2 a A line is perpendicular to the line $y = 5 - 4x$ and passes through the point (4, 2). Find the equation of the line.

 b A line is perpendicular to the line $\frac{x}{3} + \frac{y}{4} = 1$ and passes through the point (4, 1). Find the equation of the line.

3 Draw suitable diagrams to show these inequalities. Remember to leave the required region *unshaded*.

 a $x \leqslant 5$ **b** $y \geqslant -1$ **c** $x < 5$ and $y < 4$
 d $-3 \leqslant x \leqslant 2$ **e** $x > 3$ and $x < -2$

4 Write the sets of inequalities that describe the *unshaded* regions.

a
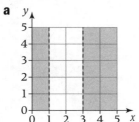

b
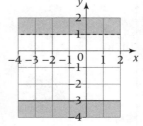

c
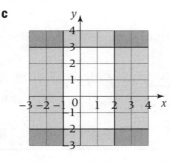

d
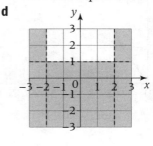

Hint: Remember that solid lines are used for $\leqslant$ and $\geqslant$ and broken lines for $<$ and $>$.

43

1 Draw a diagram to show the region of points with coordinates that satisfy the four inequalities $y \geqslant 0$, $x \geqslant 0$, $2x \leqslant 5$ and $y \leqslant x + 1$.

2 Draw a diagram to show the region of points with coordinates that satisfy the three inequalities $x > -1$, $3y < 11 - x$ and $3y > 4x + 1$.

3 The straight line L_1 has equation $y = 3x - 2$. The straight line L_2 is parallel to L_1. The straight line L_2 passes through $(2, 5)$. Find an equation of the straight line L_2.

4 Find the coordinates of the point where the graphs of $\dfrac{x}{5} + \dfrac{y}{2} = 1$ and $5y = 2x - 6$ meet.

5 Write down the three inequalities that describe the *unshaded* region.

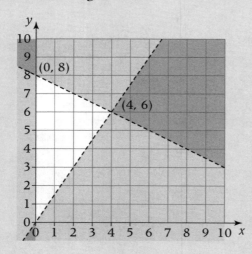

1 Work out

a $1\frac{1}{4} \times 2\frac{2}{3}$ **b** $2\frac{1}{2} \div 1\frac{1}{3}$ **c** $5\frac{3}{7} \times 3\frac{1}{2}$ **d** $2\frac{5}{8} \div 1\frac{3}{4}$

2 a Without drawing the graphs, write where these pairs of lines intersect.

i $x = 1$ and $y = 7$

ii $y = -2$ and $x = 5$

iii $x = \frac{3}{8}$ and $y = -3$

b Without drawing the graphs, calculate the coordinates of the point where the lines $y = 3x - 2$ and $y = 4 - x$ meet.

3 ABC is an isosceles triangle where AB = BC.

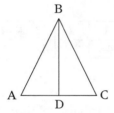

A line has been drawn from B to meet the base, AC, at D.
BD is perpendicular to AC.
Prove that triangles BAD and BDC are congruent.

Hint: Use **R**ight-angle, **H**ypotenuse, **S**ide.

4 A machine producing chocolate cake bars develops a fault. Every 10th cake bar is sub-standard. As a result of a quality control check, a sample of cake bars is taken and none are found to be sub-standard.
Is the sample most likely to have been a random or systematic sample? Explain your answer.

1 A child's push chair is available in five different fabrics. These fabrics and the probability with which they are selected by a consumer are shown in the table.

Neutrals	Checks	City Chic	Vibrant	Pure
0.42	0.11	x	$2x$	0.05

Find the missing value x and hence the missing probabilities.

2 A child has a set of building blocks, numbered 1 to 20, in a trolley. The child selects one block at random.

a Find the probability that the number on the chosen block is

   i an 8   **ii** a multiple of 4   **iii** a factor of 6
   iv a prime number   **v** the number 3 or greater than 15.

b What can you say about the pair of events in part **v**?

3 A biased dice is in the shape of a tetrahedron. The dice is rolled 100 times. The table shows the outcomes of this experiment.

Score	1	2	3	4
Frequency	48	19	16	17

a If the dice is rolled once more, find the probability that it will land on a **i** 1 **ii** 3 or 4 **iii** not 2.

b The dice is to be rolled 300 times. How many times would you expect the dice to land on a **i** 2 **ii** 1 or 4?

4 80 students are asked to choose their favourite season.

	Spring	Summer	Autumn	Winter	Total
Skiers	8			12	
Non-skiers		18	7	8	
Total	20		16		80

a Copy and complete the table.
b A student is chosen at random. Find the probability the student

   i prefers summer **ii** is a skier who prefers winter.

1 Joan carries out a statistical experiment.
She throws a dice 100 times. She scores a five 30 times.
Is the dice fair? Explain your answer.

2 A dice is rolled 30 times in order to test its fairness.
The results of this experiment are shown below.

1	3	3	5	6	2	4	4	5	2
4	2	1	4	5	1	6	4	4	4
2	3	5	4	6	4	1	5	6	4

a Work out the relative frequency of rolling each number.
b Is the dice biased? Explain your answer.
c What could you do to improve the experiment?

3 A spinner has equally sized sections numbered 1 to 8. The spinner is spun and a fair coin is thrown.

a Draw a table to show all possible outcomes.
b Find the probability of obtaining

    i the number 2 and a head
    ii a number greater than 5 and a tail
    iii an even number and a tail
    iv a prime number and a head.

4 A bag contains 4 red counters and 6 black counters.
A counter is drawn at random, its colour noted and then replaced in the bag. A second counter is then drawn.

a Find the probability of obtaining

    i a red counter on the first draw followed by a black counter on the second
    ii two red counters.

b What can you say about the events 'a red counter on the first draw' and 'a black counter on the second'?
c If the first counter is not replaced before the second counter is drawn, what can you now say about the events 'a red counter on the first draw' and 'a black counter on the second'? Explain your answer.

1. Jason and Clare play two games of Scrabble.
   The probability that Jason will win any game against Clare is 0.55. Work out the probability that Jason wins at least one game.

2. Lorna has two tins of pencils.
   Tin A contains 5 red, 6 blue and 4 yellow pencils.
   Tin B contains 3 red, 4 blue and 5 yellow pencils.
   Lorna chooses one pencil at random from each tin.
   Calculate the probability that the chosen pencils are different colours.

3. Cameron carries out a survey about the words in a book.
   He chooses a page at random and counts the letters in the first 150 words on that page. The table shows the outcomes of his experiment.

Number of letters	1	2	3	4	5	6	7	8
Frequency	8	14	35	45	30	10	5	3

   The book has 30 000 words.
   Estimate the number of 3-letter words in the book.

4. The table shows information about the teachers in a school.

	⩽5 years at school	>5 years at school
Male	20	30
Female	15	10

   a Two teachers are to be chosen at random to accept an award for their school. One male and one female teacher are to be chosen. Calculate the probability that they will both have worked at the school for ⩽5 years.
   b It is later decided to choose one teacher with ⩽5 years service and one with >5 years service to the school. Calculate the probability that both teachers are male.

1 Copy and complete this table.

Fraction	Decimal	Percentage
$\frac{3}{5}$		
	0.04	
	0.1875	45%
$\frac{7}{8}$		

2 a Sketch the line graph $2y = x - 6$.
  b Find the equation of a line which is parallel to $2y = x - 6$ and passes through (4, 4). Sketch this new line on the same set of axes.

3 The sector shown is folded to form a cone.
Find the curved surface area of the cone.

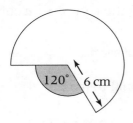

120° 6 cm

4 Two dice are thrown and the results added.
  a Draw a table to show all possible outcomes of the total of the two dice.
  b Work out the probability of obtaining a total of 9 on one throw of these dice.

Do not use a calculator for questions 1 and 2 in this exercise.

1 Alice surveys her primary school class and finds that 21 out of the 30 children have at least one sibling and 12 of the children do not have a pet. Give your answers as fractions in their lowest terms.

   a What proportion of the children have at least one sibling?

   b What proportion of the children have a pet?

   c What is the ratio of children with siblings to children without siblings? Give this ratio in its simplest form.

2 Samantha spends $\frac{3}{5}$ of her monthly salary on tax, her mortgage and her regular bills. She spends $\frac{1}{6}$ of her monthly salary on food bills and $\frac{1}{12}$ on her car payments. The rest she spends on shoes.

   a What proportion of her monthly salary does Samantha spend on shoes?

   b If Samantha earns £2400 a month, write down the amounts that she pays for
     i tax, mortgage and bills   **ii** shoes.

3 The cost of 8 tins of beans is £2.80. Find the cost of 3 tins of beans. Show all your working.

   Hint: Use the unitary method and find the price of one tin.

4 The mass of gold, g, is directly proportional to its volume, v.

   a Given that 200 cm^3 of gold has a mass of 3864 g, find a formula connecting g and v.

   b Find the mass of a gold bar, in kilograms, with dimensions 20 cm by 8 cm by 4 cm.

   c Find the volume of a gold bar with a mass of 46.368 kg. Suggest a reasonable set of dimensions for this gold bar.

1 The variable y is inversely proportional to the variable x. Write the effect on y if x is

  a multiplied by 2   **b** divided by 5
  c multiplied by 0.25   **d** divided by 0.8

2 y is inversely proportional to x. If $y = 20$ when $x = 16$, find

  a a formula for y in terms of x
  b the value of y when $x = 10$
  c the value of x when $y = 15$.

3 The number of people, n, required to build a wall is inversely proportional to the time taken, t.

  a Given that it takes 10 people 4 hours to build this wall, find a formula connecting t and n.
  b How long would it take 8 people to build this wall?
  c How many people are required to build the wall in just 20 minutes?

4 A bank pays compound interest at 4.5%. Find the amount of money in an account after 5 years if the original investment is £3000. Give your answer to the nearest penny.

5 Anna buys a car in 2003 that depreciates by 12% per year. In 2005 the car is worth £13 552.

  a What did Anna pay for the car?
  b What will the car be worth in 2010? Give your answer to 3 significant figures.

1 In the UK in 2001 there were 95 males for every 100 females in the population.

   a Write this as a ratio of males to females.
Give your answer in its simplest terms.

   b What proportion of the population was female?
Give your answer as a fraction in its simplest form.

   c If there were 58.8 million people in the UK in 2001, how many males were there? Give your answer to 3 significant figures.

2 In a class, the ratio of girls to boys is 5 : 4. There are 15 girls in this class. Work out the number of boys.

3 Two work colleagues, Bill and Ben, share a bonus of £5000 in the ratio 3 : 2. Ben decides to share his portion of the money between himself and the two members of his support team in the ratio 5 : 2 : 1.
How much does Ben take home?

4 In 2001, Britain had a population of 58.8 million. If the population of Britain is increasing at, on average, an annual rate of 0.4%, calculate an estimate for the population of Britain in 2005. Give your answer to 3 significant figures.

5 If a varies as b and $a = 6$ when $b = 10$, find

   a the value of a when $b = 18$

   b the value of b when $a = 9$.

1 Philip's van depreciates in value by 8% each year. After four years the van is worth £9170.

    a What was the original cost of the van?

    b What was the overall percentage depreciation of the van after 4 years?

    c If the van continues to depreciate at the same rate, after how many years will the van be worth less than £5000?

2 Choose either 'parallel' or 'perpendicular' to complete these sentences.

    a The line $y = 2x + 1$ is   to the line $y = 2x - 3$.

    b The line $y = 6 - x$ is   to the line $y = 12 - x$.

    c The line $y = 2x - 5$ is   to the line $y = 7 - \frac{1}{2}x$.

    d The line $3y = 4 - x$ is   to the line $y = 3x + 2$.

    e The line $\dfrac{x}{3} + \dfrac{y}{4} = 1$ is   to the line $\dfrac{x}{6} + \dfrac{y}{8} = 1$.

3 A bowling alley wants to buy chutes down which children can bowl in order to direct their aim at the pins. Children's bowling balls have a surface area of 5025 cm². The chute must have 3 cm room around the ball in order to allow it to move freely.

    What is the minimum diameter the chute can have?

    Hint: Rearrange the formula for the surface area of a sphere and hence find the diameter of the bowling ball.

4 Suggest improvements to these questions for use in a questionnaire.

    a How many times do you go on holiday each year?

    b What is your favourite holiday destination?

1 Which of these pairs of triangles are congruent? Give reasons for your answers.

a

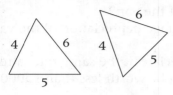

b

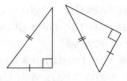

c

d

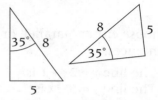

2 ABCD is a square. Prove that triangles ABC and ACD are congruent.

3 Prove that triangle PQR is congruent to triangle RST.

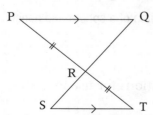

1 Copy this diagram.

  a Enlarge parallelogram
    ABCD by scale factor 2
    about centre (0, 0).
    Label the image
    A'B'C'D'.

  b Enlarge parallelogram
    ABCD by scale factor
    $-\frac{1}{2}$ about centre (0, 0).
    Label the image
    A"B"C"D".

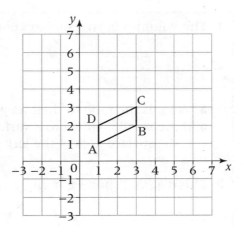

2 Triangle A'B'C' is an
enlargement of triangle ABC.

  a Copy the diagram and,
    showing clearly any pencil
    lines you use to help you,
    find the centre of
    enlargement.

  b Write the scale factor of this
    enlargement.

  c What is the scale factor of the
    enlargement that maps
    triangle A'B'C' back onto
    triangle ABC?
    What do you notice about
    this and your answer to part **b**?

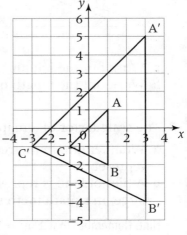

3 Are triangles ABC and PQR similar triangles?
Show your working.

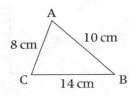
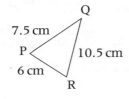

1 The volumes of two similar cubes are in the ratio 8 : 27.

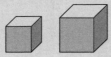

    a What is the ratio of their lengths?
    b If the smaller cube has a surface area of 384 cm², what is the surface area of the larger cube?

2 This diagram shows a triangle PST.

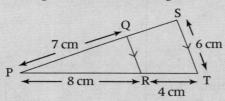

    a Work out the length of QR.
    b Work out the length of PS.

3 The scale factor of a map is 1 : 20 000.

    a What length, in metres, does 1 cm on the map represent?
    b A plot of land is represented by 2 cm² on the map. How large, in square metres, is the actual plot of land?

    Hint: Remember that 1 m² = 100 × 100 cm².

4 Find the missing side.
    a

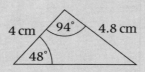

    b

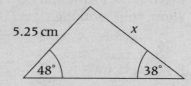

1 In a primary school class, $\frac{1}{5}$ of the students have black hair, $\frac{3}{10}$ of the students have blonde hair and $\frac{7}{15}$ of the students have brown hair. The rest have red hair.

   a What proportion of the class have red hair?

   b If there are 30 students in the class, how many have

      i black hair   **ii** brown hair?

2 Simplify these fractional multiplications and divisions.

   a $\dfrac{x+3}{2} \times \dfrac{6}{x^2 - 2x - 15}$ **b** $\dfrac{x^2 - 4}{24} \div \dfrac{x^2 - 7x - 18}{8}$

3 Two similar cylinders have diameters of 5 cm and 8 cm.

5 cm   8 cm

If the capacity of the larger cylinder is 384 cm^3, find the capacity of the smaller cylinder.

4 Xavier has a packet of seeds that will produce flowering plants. Each week over a 5 week period, Xavier plants 20 seeds.
This table shows the number of seeds that produce flowers out of each batch of seeds planted.

Week	1	2	3	4	5
No. of plants with flowers	12	11	15	10	12

   a For each week, work out the relative frequency of a plant producing flowers.

   b Work out the best estimate of the probability of a plant flowering.

N5 HW2 Index laws

1 Work out these calculations, giving your answer in index form.

a $3^4 \times 3^5$ **b** $2^5 \times 2^2$ **c** $a^4 \div a$

d $5^6 \div 5^6$ **e** $4^2 \times 4^2 \times 4^2$ **f** $x^2 \times x^3 \times x^4$

g $6^5 \div 6^3 \times 6$ **h** $8^2 \times 8^6 \div 8^3$

2 Simplify these expressions, giving your answer in index form.

a $\dfrac{3^5 \times 3^2}{3^4}$ **b** $\dfrac{(5^3)^4}{5^2 \times 5^5}$ **c** $\dfrac{(x^8 \div x^3)^2}{x^4 \times x}$ **d** $y^3 \times \dfrac{y^2 \times y^6}{(y^4)^2}$

3 Solve these equations.

a $2^x = 16$ **b** $y^2 = 5^4$ **c** $64 = (2^a)^2$ **d** $72 = b^3 \times 3^b$

4 Pair these cards together if they show equivalent numbers. Which is the odd card out?

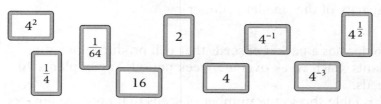

5 Evaluate each of these.

a $8^{\frac{2}{3}}$ **b** $16^{\frac{3}{2}}$

c $100^{\frac{5}{2}}$ **d** $81^{-\frac{1}{4}}$

e $64^{-\frac{1}{2}}$ **e** $25^{-\frac{3}{2}}$

1 Which of these numbers are irrational?

Number	✓ or ✗
$\sqrt{9}$	
5π	
$\frac{4}{7}$	
$\sqrt[3]{5}$	
$\sqrt{15}$	

2 The numbers 1 and 64 both have a rational square root and a rational cube root.

Number, x	Square root of x	Cube root of x
1	1	1
64	8	4

a Can you find the next number that has both a rational square root and a rational cube root? Add it to the table.
b By considering the two right hand columns of the table, work out the next number that follows this criterion.

3 Evaluate these without using a calculator.
a $\sqrt{2} \times \sqrt{8}$ **b** $\sqrt{18} \times \sqrt{2}$ **c** $\sqrt{5} \times \sqrt{20}$ **d** $\sqrt{45} \times \sqrt{5}$

4 Rationalise the denominator of each of these fractions.

a $\dfrac{1}{\sqrt{5}}$ **b** $\dfrac{2}{\sqrt{7}}$

c $\dfrac{3}{1 + \sqrt{10}}$ **d** $\dfrac{1 - \sqrt{3}}{1 + \sqrt{3}}$

5 Simplify these expressions.
a $2\sqrt{5} + \sqrt{45}$ **b** $\sqrt{20}(1 + \sqrt{5})$ **c** $(5 + \sqrt{3})(5 - \sqrt{3})$

1 a Multiplication is distributive over addition. Show how this idea can be used to calculate 34×21.
b Multiplication is distributive over subtraction. Show how this idea can be used to calculate 34×18.

Hint: The distributive law for multiplication states that
$a(b + c) = ab + ac$.

2 a Factorise $a^2 - b^2$ into double brackets.
b Use your answer to part **a** to work out $7.8^2 - 2.2^2$.

3 a Expand and simplify $(p + q)^2$.
b Hence or otherwise, find the value of
$$1.36^2 + 2 \times 1.36 \times 3.64 + 3.64^2$$

4 Simplify

a $\dfrac{p^3}{p^5}$

b $\dfrac{m^8}{m^4 \times m}$

5 Evaluate

a $25^{\frac{1}{2}}$

b $81^{-\frac{3}{4}}$

6 Solve these equations.

a $3^4 = 81$

b $y^8 = 256$

c $a^2 = 4^6$

1 Angela, Rajat and Ayesha have savings in the ratio 5 : 4 : 1. If Rajat has £2400, calculate the amount of money that Angela and Ayesha have in savings.

2 Find the equation of the straight line joining these pairs of points.

a (0, 1) and (3, 10)
b (2, −1) and (5, −7)
c (−3, 1) and (3, 3)

3 Sort these rectangles into pairs of similar shapes. All measurements are in centimetres.

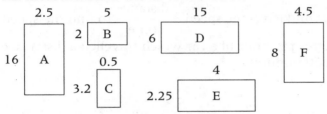

4 This two-way table shows the preferred method for cooking potatoes of 100 chefs. Each chef could choose only one method.

	Mashing	Chipping	Roasting	Total
Female		12		40
Male	12			
Total	28		32	100

a Copy and complete the table.
b A chef is chosen at random. Write the probability that

  i the chef's preferred method of cooking potatoes is roasting
  ii the chef is male and prefers mashing potatoes.

c If this is a typical group of chefs, how many of the chefs in a hotel employing 150 chefs would you expect to be female?

1 Copy and complete this table. Choose from the words *identity, equation* or *formula* for the right-hand column. The first one has been completed for you.

	Identity, equation or formula?
$4x^2(x-3) = 4x^3 - 12x^2$	*identity*
$x(x+6) = 40$	
$x^3 = -125$	
$V = \frac{4}{3}\pi r^3$	
$3x^4(1-x) = 3x^4 - 3x^5$	
$A = 2\pi rh$	

2 Use the formula average speed $= \dfrac{\text{distance}}{\text{time}}$ to find the speed in kilometres per hour of a car which travelled a distance of 25 km in 20 minutes.

3 Use the formula $r = \sqrt{\dfrac{A}{\pi}}$ to find the radius of a circle with area 64 cm^2. Give your answer to 3 significant figures.

4 Make x the subject of these formulae.

a $ax + b = c$ **b** $\dfrac{x}{p} + q = t$

c $m + x = w - n$ **d** $a = \sqrt{bx - n}$

e $p^2 x + a = n$ **f** $r = \dfrac{ab - x}{c}$

g $\dfrac{y}{x} + t^2 = s$ **h** $r = \dfrac{n}{b + ax}$

1 Three of these formulae are rearrangements of another three. One is the odd one out. By showing all your working, find the odd one out.

$$a - \frac{b}{x} = c^2$$

$$\frac{a}{c^2 x} = b$$

$$b = a(x^2 - c)$$

$$x = b - ac^2$$

$$ac^2 + x = b$$

$$x = \frac{b}{a - c^2}$$

$$x^2 = \frac{b}{a} + c$$

2 k appears twice in each of these formulae. Collect the terms in k on one side and rearrange to make k the subject of the formula.

a $ak + b = ck + d$

b $kx + 6 = 2 - ky$

c $p(k + a) = q(b - k)$

d $\dfrac{3 + k}{3 - k} = x$

e $k + x = \dfrac{2k + 3}{x}$

f $\sqrt{\dfrac{k - p}{k - q}} = \dfrac{1}{2}$

3 Find a counter-example to disprove each of these statements.

a All prime numbers are odd.

b The reciprocal of x is always less than x.

c Two irrational numbers will always give an irrational number when multiplied together.

4 a Prove that the sum of any two odd numbers is always even.

b Prove that the sum of an odd number and an even number is always odd.

1 a Rearrange the cosine rule

$$a^2 = b^2 + c^2 - 2bc \cos A$$

to make cos A the subject.
Show all steps in your working.

b Hence find angle A in this triangle.

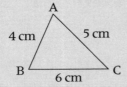

2 Prove that the product of two odd numbers is always odd.

Hint: Let the two numbers be $2n + 1$ and $2m + 1$.

3 Prove that angles of a triangle add up to $180°$.

Hint: Use the fact that angles on a straight line add up to $180°$, and also use corresponding and alternate angles.

4 Given that this triangle is right-angled, prove that
$x^2 - 16x + 34 = 0$

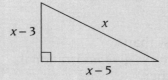

1 In the summer sale, all clothes have a 20% discount.

   a What is the sale price of a pair of trousers that cost £85 before the sale?

In the last week of the sale, these sale prices are reduced by a further 20%.

   b What is the price of the trousers now?

   c What is the overall percentage reduction of the pair of trousers after both discounts have been applied?

2 Find the *n*th term of these sequences.

   a 4, 7, 10, 13, 16, ...
   b 2, 7, 12, 17, 22, ...
   c 4, 9, 16, 25, 36, ...
   d 3, 5, 9, 15, 23, ...

3 Work out the missing angles, giving reasons for your answers.

   a

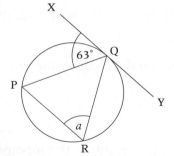

   b

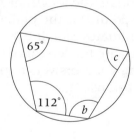

4 Lynda is looking for her reading glasses. The probability that they are in her handbag is $\frac{3}{5}$. The probability that they are by her bed is $\frac{2}{9}$. Find the probability that Lynda's reading glasses are

   a either in her handbag or by her bed
   b lost! That is, in neither of these places.

What assumption have you made throughout this question?

1 Calculate the length of the missing sides.

a

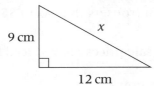

9 cm

x

12 cm

b 15 mm

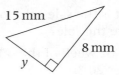

8 mm

y

c

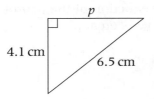

p

4.1 cm

6.5 cm

d

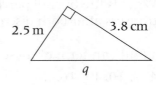

2.5 m

3.8 cm

q

2 A triangle has vertices A = (1, 1), B = (4, 4) and C = (5, 0).

  a Sketch a diagram of this triangle.
  b Calculate the length of AB.
  c The point D is the midpoint of the line AB. Work out the coordinates of point D.
  d Calculate the length of CD.
  e Using your answers to parts **b** and **d**, calculate the area of the triangle.

3 Using the tangent ratio, calculate the length of the missing sides of these triangles.

a

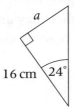

a

16 cm 24°

b 9.3 mm

41° b

c

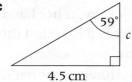

59°

c

4.5 cm

Finding angles and sides using trigonometry

1 Find the missing sides in each of these right-angled triangles, giving your answers to 3 significant figures.

a

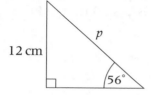

12 cm
p
56°

b

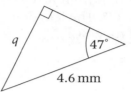

q
47°
4.6 mm

c

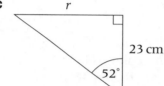

r
23 cm
52°

d

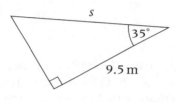

s
35°
9.5 m

2 Find the missing angles in each of these right-angled triangles, giving your answers to 3 significant figures.

a

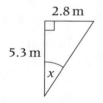

2.8 m
5.3 m
x

b

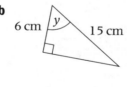

6 cm
y
15 cm

c

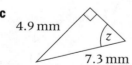

4.9 mm
z
7.3 mm

d

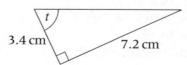

t
3.4 cm
7.2 cm

3 Phil measures the angle of elevation from the ground where he is lying to the top of a cliff as 23°. He is exactly 60 m from the base of the cliff. By sketching a diagram and using trigonometry, work out the height of the cliff.

1 A flagpole BD is secured by two ropes from the top of the flagpole to the ground at points A and C. The angle of elevation of B from A is 53°. The angle of elevation of B from C is 34°. The length of rope BA is 10 m. Find the length of rope BC.

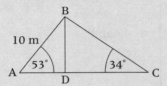

2 In the triangle PQR, RS is perpendicular to PQ. PR = 8.2 cm, QS = 9.5 cm and angle RQS = 38°. Calculate *x* to 1 decimal place.

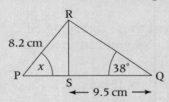

3 ABC is a right-angled triangle.
CD : DB = 1 : 2
Angle ABC = 43° and
AC = 14 m.
Calculate angle CAD.

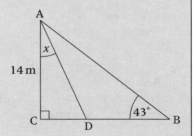

4 An isosceles triangle has sides of length 6 cm, 6 cm and 4 cm.
Calculate the interior angles and the height of the triangle.

1 The mass, w, of copper, is directly proportional to its volume, v.

  a Given that 150 cm^3 of copper has a mass of 1344 g, find the value of k in the formula $w = kv$.

  b What property of copper does the value k represent?

  c Find the mass of a solid copper rod of radius 1.5 cm and length 30 cm.

  d Find the volume of a solid copper rod with a mass of 2.912 kg.

2 A rectangle has width $= \dfrac{2x^2 + 7x - 15}{4}$ and length $= \dfrac{48}{2x - 3}$.

The area of this rectangle is 96 cm^2.

By forming an equation in x, find the value of x and hence the dimensions of the rectangle.

3 Calculate the length of the missing side.

  a 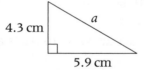   **b**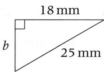

Give your answers to 3 significant figures.

4 Annie recorded the time taken, to the nearest minute, by a sample of students to complete a Sudoku puzzle.

35   38   38   40   41   43   46   50   52   55   60

  a Write **i** the lower quartile   **ii** the upper quartile.

  b Draw a box plot to represent this data.

1 By rounding each of the values in these calculations to 1 significant figure, find an approximate answer.

    a $\dfrac{86.7 - 21.4}{5.95 + 4.18}$ **b** $\dfrac{42.71 \times 0.099}{2.03^3}$

    c $\sqrt{\dfrac{18.2^2}{0.82 \times 4.56}}$ **d** $\dfrac{3.1^4}{0.088 - 0.008\,76}$

2 Explain why rounding each of the values in these calculations to 1 significant figure would *not* be an appropriate method for estimating the answer.

    a $\dfrac{21.4 \times 5.15}{0.84 - 0.75}$ **b** $(4.56 - 4.32)^2$

3 Use standard form approximations to find an estimate for these calculations.

    a $(81\,500 \div 194)^3$ **b** $\dfrac{4420 \times 0.8}{0.52 \times 0.043}$

    c Use your calculator to find the exact answers to parts **a** and **b**.

4 Calculate these, leaving π in your answers.

    a the area of a circle of diameter 14 cm

    b the volume of a hemisphere of radius 6 m

    c the radius of a circle of circumference 18 mm

5 Evaluate these, leaving your answers in surd form.

    a $\sqrt{3}(2 - \sqrt{3})$ **b** $(8 + \sqrt{5})(3 - \sqrt{5})$

1 Jonathan took measurements around his school.
Are these values sensible?

  a The height of the cherry tree outside the maths
building = 4.5 m.

  b The weight of an apple from the school canteen = 1.6 kg.

  c The height of the door into the French room = 215 cm.

  d The capacity of the sink in the wash room = 2.3 litres.

2 Write the upper and lower bounds of these calculations.

  a The radius of a circle measured as 4.5 cm to 1 decimal
place

  b The area of a rectangle with dimensions 12 cm and 6.8 cm
taken to 2 significant figures

  c The width of a parallelogram which has an area of 20 cm^2
(to the nearest square centimetre) and a length of 8.45 cm
(to 2 decimal places)

  d The speed, in km/h, of a car which travels 35 km (to the
nearest kilometre) in 30 minutes (to the nearest minute.)

3 Use a calculator to evaluate these. Give each answer to an
appropriate degree of accuracy by considering the degree of
accuracy in the question.

  a $(5.2 \times 10^6) \times (8.2 \times 10^3)$ **b** $(3.45 \times 10^4) \div (1.52 \times 10^{-2})$

  c $(8.35 \times 10^8) \times (6.12 \times 10^{-5})$ **d** $(7.1 \times 10^3) \div (8.7 \times 10^5)$

4 Find the value of these using a calculator. Give each answer
to an appropriate degree of accuracy by considering the
degree of accuracy in the question.

  a $\sqrt{41.2^2 + 7.62^2}$ **b** $\sqrt{1.3^2 + 2.7^2 - 2 \times 1.3 \times 2.7 \times \cos 48°}$

  c $4\frac{1}{3} \div 1\frac{3}{7}$ **d** $\dfrac{-7 + \sqrt{7^2 - (4 \times 3 \times -6)}}{2 \times 3}$

1 Evaluate these *without* using a calculator. Show each stage in your working clearly.

a $\dfrac{-5.3 + (4 \times 3.2)}{5 \times 0.3}$ **b** $2.5^2 - \dfrac{3.05 + 1.15}{\sqrt{0.64}}$

2 Grace has a toothbrush holder that is 20.2 cm long, to the nearest millimetre. She buys a new toothbrush that measures 20 cm to the nearest centimetre. Explain why Grace's new toothbrush may not fit into her toothbrush holder.

3 Work out the missing side of this right-angled triangle, leaving your answer in surd form.

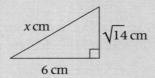

x cm

$\sqrt{14}$ cm

6 cm

4 Calculate

$$\dfrac{2.45 \times 1.36^2 - 3.48 \cos 24°}{\sqrt{8.24 + 0.428}}$$

1 Find the value of n if

$8^{n+1} = 32$

Hint: Use indices and rewrite 8 as a power of 2 and 32 as a power of 2.
On the left hand side apply the rule $(x^m)^n = x^{mn}$.
Compare the index numbers.

2 Draw a diagram to show the region of points with coordinates that satisfy the four inequalities
$y \geqslant 0, x \geqslant 0, y \leqslant 5 - x$ and $y \geqslant x - 1$.

3 Find the missing sides and angles in these right-angled triangles.

a

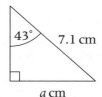

43°   7.1 cm

a cm

b

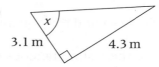

x

3.1 m   4.3 m

c

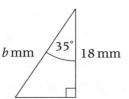

b mm   35°   18 mm

d

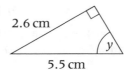

2.6 cm

y

5.5 cm

4 a A number is selected at random from the numbers 1 to 20 inclusive.
Find the probability that it is either a multiple of 4 or a prime number.

b What can you say about the outcomes 'select a multiple of 4' and 'select a prime number'?

1 The perpendicular height of a triangle is 3 cm less than the length of its base. The area of the triangle is 27 cm². Form a quadratic equation to represent the information and solve to find the dimensions of the triangle.

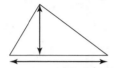

2 The area of a rectangle is 21 cm² and its perimeter is 20 cm. The length of the rectangle is x cm and its width is y cm.

   a Write equations for the area and perimeter in terms of x and y.

   b Use substitution in order to form a quadratic in one variable.

   c Solve to find the dimensions of the rectangle.

3 Solve these simultaneous equations by the elimination method.

   a $2x + 3y = 21$ **b** $2p + 5q = 1$ **c** $3s - 7t = 27$
       $x - y = 8$ $3p - 2q = 11$ $5s + 3t = 1$

   d $\quad\quad y = 4 - x$ **e** $2y = 18 - 4x$ **f** $4a - 2b + 2 = 0$
      $3x + 44 = 5y$ $0 = 3x - 2y + 4$ $3b - 3a + 3 = 0$

4 Sarah keeps her receipts from a coffee bar. She observes that on one visit she bought 2 lattes and a piece of carrot cake costing £3.25 and on another visit she bought 4 lattes and 4 pieces of carrot cake costing £8.20. The prices have remained stable. What is the cost of a latte and the cost of a piece of carrot cake?

5 In a right-angled triangle, the difference between the other two angles is 12°. Find the two missing angles.

   Hint: What is the sum of the two missing angles?

1 Solve these simultaneous equations.

a $x^2 + y = 88$
  $y = 7$

b $6y - x^2 = 23$
  $y = 8$

c $x^2 + y^2 = 106$
  $x + y = 14$

d $y = x^2 + 3$
  $y = 3x + 7$

e $p = 3q^2$
  $p = 7q - 2$

f $a^2 + b^2 = 113$
  $2b - a = 9$

2 Find the points of intersection of these curves and lines. Show each solution as a coordinate and give your answers to 3 significant figures where appropriate.

a $y = x^2 - 2x - 2$
  $x = 2y + 1$

b $x^2 + 3y^2 = 13$
  $x + y = 1$

c $x^2 + y^2 = 7$
  $3x - y = 4$

3 Write the equation of a circle with
  a centre (0, 0), radius 3   **b** centre (0, 0), radius $\sqrt{3}$
  c centre (0, 0), passing through (3, 4).

4 The diagram shows the circle with equation $x^2 + y^2 = 8$.

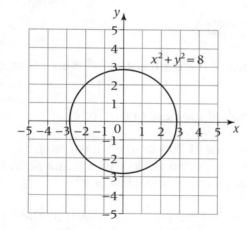

a Copy the graph, extending x and y axes to 8 and −8, and sketch the line with equation $y = 8 - 2x$.
b Explain, by referring to the graph, why the simultaneous equations $x^2 + y^2 = 8$ and $y = 8 - 2x$ can have no solution.

1 Write an inequality to represent each of these statements, stating the meaning of any letters used.

   a Due to fire safety regulations, the maximum number of people in the theatre at any one time is 354.

   b The temperature of the freezer must remain below $-4\,°C$.

   c Transactions of £5 or less are not permitted.

2 Solve these inequalities.

   a $5x - 9 < 11$　　　　**b** $3x + 1 \geqslant 5x - 3$　　**c** $y^2 \leqslant 9$

   d $2(3 - y) \geqslant 3(y + 3)$　**e** $2x^2 - 3 < 29$

3 The diagram shows a cone with slanted height = 4 cm and radius of base = r cm.

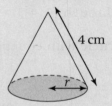

4 cm

r

   a The total surface area of the cone is 40 cm^2. Show that

     $\pi r^2 + 4\pi r - 40 = 0$

   b Hence, find the radius of the base of the cone.

4 Shamoon covers a distance of 200 m in 65 seconds. He jogs part of the way at 4 m/s and walks the rest at a pace of 2 m/s. How far does he travel at each speed?

5 Maya said that the line $y = 4$ cuts the circle given by the equation $x^2 + y^2 = 4$ at two points.

   a Luke said that she was wrong and sketched a graph to explain. What did this graph look like?

   b Bill agreed that she was wrong and proved his point algebraically. How did he do this?

1 Work out these, giving your answer in index form.

a $5^3 \times 5^6$ **b** $4^5 \div 4$ **c** $x^2 \times x^4 \times x^8$

d $\dfrac{2^9}{2^4 \times 2^3}$ **e** $\dfrac{a^5 \times a^9}{(a^2)^3}$ **f** $\dfrac{y}{(y^{\frac{1}{2}} \times y^{\frac{1}{2}})^3}$

2 A rectangular garden has an area of 40 m^2 and a perimeter of 26 m. The length of the garden is a cm and its width is b cm.

a Form two equations involving a and b.

b Solve these equations simultaneously in order to find the length and width of the garden.

3 **a** Copy the graph and enlarge triangle ABC by scale factor 3 about centre (0, 3).
Label the image A′B′C′.

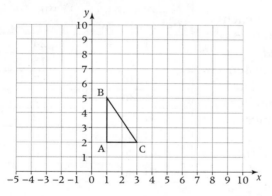

b On the same graph, enlarge triangle ABC by scale factor −1 about centre (0, 3).
Label the image A″B″C″.

4 Lucy is offered a biscuit from each of two tins.
The first tin contains 6 chocolate and 4 plain biscuits.
The second tin contains 5 chocolate and 10 plain biscuits.
Lucy chooses one biscuit at random from each tin. Calculate the probability that the chosen biscuits are different types.

1 Kath recorded the masses of 50 two-year-olds.

Mass, m (kg)	Frequency	Midpoint	Midpoint × frequency
$10 < m \leqslant 11$	5	10.5	$10.5 \times 5 = 52.5$
$11 < m \leqslant 12$	15	11.5	
$12 < m \leqslant 13$	17		
$13 < m \leqslant 14$	9		
$14 < m \leqslant 15$	4		
Total			

a Copy and complete the table to find an estimate for the mean.

b Find
  i the modal class   **ii** the class containing the median.

c Work out an estimate for the range.

2 The table shows the number of words in each of the first 50 sentences of the novel *Pride and Prejudice* by Jane Austen.

No. of words per sentence	Frequency
1–10	24
11–20	15
21–30	7
31–40	1
41–50	2
51–60	0
61–70	0
71–80	1

a Calculate an estimate for the mean number of words per sentence.

b Is the mean a good representation of the average number of words per sentence? Explain your answer.

3 A class of 30 students is challenged to time one minute. The students are asked to stand and then sit down after they believe one minute has passed. These are the actual times, in seconds, at which they sat down.

75 53 72 77 59 42 65 52 70 58 70 45 63 41 49
58 62 43 48 57 61 55 62 59 68 73 63 61 67 71

a Construct a frequency table for the data.
b Construct a frequency polygon for the data.

1 A waiter kept a record of his tips in pounds per month over a period of 12 months.

Jan	Feb	Mar	Apr	May	Jun	Jul	Aug	Sep	Oct	Nov	Dec
30	34	35	60	75	84	92	100	72	48	32	95

Draw a time series graph to represent these data.

2 The table shows information about Ruby's quarterly telephone bills over a two-year period.

	Jan–Mar	Apr–Jun	Jul–Sep	Oct–Dec
2004	£123	£97	£84	£116
2005	£139	£105	£92	£124

  a Draw a time series graph for these data.
  b Calculate four-point moving averages for these data and plot them on the same graph.
  c Comment on the trend shown by the moving averages.

3 A small knitwear company believes that 'tank-tops' are becoming trendy and, to investigate, decides to look at the number of tank-tops sold over the last two years.

	Spring Collection	Summer Collection	Autumn Collection	Winter Collection
2004	102	43	88	177
2005	126	49	100	195

  a Calculate the four-point moving averages for these data.
  b Plot the data on a graph.
  c Describe the trend shown by this graph and comment on the beliefs of the company.

1 A retailer keeps a record of its
television sales in one week.
The table shows sales which are
£1000 or less.

Cost, £c	Frequency
$0 < c \leqslant 200$	5
$200 < c \leqslant 400$	12
$400 < c \leqslant 600$	43
$600 < c \leqslant 800$	25
$800 < c \leqslant 1000$	15

  a Calculate an estimate for the
mean from this table.
  b Find the class interval in which the median lies.
  c There was only one other television sale this week: a
plasma screen television costing £2700. If this amount
were included, would the class interval in which the
median lies change?

2 A small toyshop kept a record of the amount spent in
each transaction during December and January.

December

Amount, £p	Frequency
$0 < p \leqslant 20$	12
$20 < p \leqslant 40$	30
$40 < p \leqslant 60$	38
$60 < p \leqslant 80$	64
$80 < p \leqslant 100$	56

January

Amount, £p	Frequency
$0 < p \leqslant 20$	24
$20 < p \leqslant 40$	45
$40 < p \leqslant 60$	18
$60 < p \leqslant 80$	13
$80 < p \leqslant 100$	0

  a Draw frequency polygons for these data.
  b For each set of data work out
    i the modal class   **ii** the range.
  c Use your answers to make comparisons, with reasons,
between the amounts spent in December and January.

3 The table gives information about the percentage of the
population who smoked between 1974 and 2000.

Year	1974	1978	1982	1986	1990	1994	1998	2000
%	45	40	35	33	30	27	28	27

  a Draw a time series graph to represent these data.
  b Calculate five-point moving averages for these data and
plot them.
  c Use your results to estimate the percentage of the
population who smoked in 2004.

1 Simplify these surds.

a $\dfrac{1}{\sqrt{3}}$

b $\dfrac{1}{\sqrt{5}}$

c $\dfrac{3}{\sqrt{7}}$

d $\sqrt{20}$

e $\sqrt{50}$

f $\dfrac{1}{2\sqrt{3}}$

2 Change the subject of these equations to that given in brackets.

a $y = 3x + 8$ (x)

b $s = \dfrac{2t}{3} - r$ (t)

c $pq - r = s$ (q)

d $a = \dfrac{b}{c}$ (c)

e $2p - q = t$ (q)

f $\dfrac{a(b - c)}{x} = y$ (a)

g $p(q - r) = a(q + b)$ (q)

h $a(x - b) = \dfrac{x}{c}$ (x)

3 The heights of two bottles of water are in the ratio 2 : 5.
The smaller bottle has a capacity of 320 ml.
What is the capacity of the larger bottle?

4 Gemma interviewed her class and recorded the length of
time each student had spent on their mathematics
homework. Copy and complete the table and draw a
cumulative frequency curve to represent the data. Use the
curve to estimate the median time taken.

Time, t (min)	Frequency, f	t	Cumulative frequency
$0 \leqslant t < 10$	2	< 10	
$10 \leqslant t < 20$	8	< 20	
$20 \leqslant t < 30$	15		
$30 \leqslant t < 40$	5		

1 Calculate the length of the sides marked with letters.

a

12 mm

19 mm

x

b

6.2 cm

38°

y

c

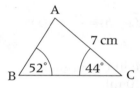

p

46°

5.8 m

d

22°

q

9.1 cm

2 Find AB.

A

7 cm

52°   44°

B   C

3 In triangle PQR, angle QPR = 54°, angle PQR = 32° and
PR = 10 mm. Find the two missing sides of the triangle.

Hint: Find angle QRP.

4 In triangle ABC, angle BAC = 63°, AB = 3.3 cm and
BC = 4.1 cm. Find the two missing angles of the triangle.

1 Use the cosine rule to find the missing sides, marked with letters.

a
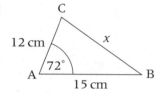

b
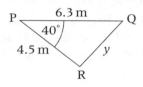

2 Use the cosine rule to find the missing angles, marked θ.

a
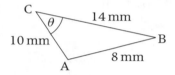

b
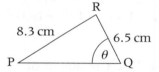

3 Quadville is 45 km from Parallelford on a bearing of 124°. Rhombustown is 60 km due south of Parallelford.
By sketching a diagram and using the cosine rule, find the distance from Rhombustown to Quadville.

4 A triangle ABC has angle ABC = 72°, angle CAB = 64° and BC = 9.3 mm. Find the perimeter of the triangle.

Hint: Find angle ACB and use the sine rule.

5 Find all three angles of triangle ABC.

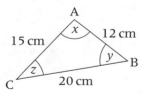

1 In the cuboid, PQ = 7 m,
QR = 3 m and RS = 4 m.

   a Find PS.

   b Find the angle PS makes with
the base of the cuboid.

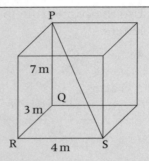

2 Work out the distance between the points
(5, 4, 6) and (2, −1, 4).

3 **a** Find the height of XY.

   b Find the angle XAY.

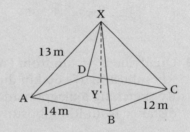

4 ABCDEF is a wedge.
The rectangular base
ABCD is perpendicular
to the back face CDEF.
EF = 6 cm, BC = 5 cm
and CF = 3 cm.

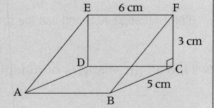

   a Calculate the length BF.

   b Calculate the length BE.

   c Calculate the angle EBD.

1 Make x the subject of these formulae.

  a $x + ab = c$ **b** $p^3x - q = r$ **c** $d + \dfrac{x}{c} = f$

  d $\sqrt{x + k} = 4$ **e** $\sqrt{(n^2 + x^2)} = m$

2 x appears twice in each of these formulae. Collect the terms in x on one side and rearrange to make x the subject of the formula.

  a $px + q = ax + b$ **b** $k(x - m) = tx$

  c $\dfrac{x + p}{x - p} = A$ **d** $x(m - n) = p - x$

3 In the cuboid AB = 8 cm, BC = 9 cm and DC = 12 cm.

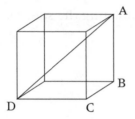

  a Find the distance BD.
  b Find the angle AD makes with the base.

4 John kept a record of the takings he made from selling hot soup in his shop during a two year period.

	Jan–Mar	Apr–Jun	Jul–Sep	Oct–Dec
2003	£188	£102	£124	£205
2004	£210	£112	£142	£228

  a Draw a time series graph to represent these data.
  b Calculate four-point moving averages for these data and plot them on the same graph.
  c Describe the trend shown by the moving averages.

1 Use the discriminant to decide

   i the number of solutions that each quadratic equation has

   ii whether or not it is possible to factorise.

   a $x^2 - 6x - 27 = 0$ **b** $4x^2 - 4x + 1 = 0$

   c $5x - 2x^2 + 12 = 0$ **d** $x^2 + 7x - 2 = 0$

   e $3x^2 = 2x - 5$ **f** $x(5x - 8) = 3$

2 Solve all quadratic equations in question **1** that can be solved.

3 Solve these quadratic equations by completing the square. Leave your answers in surd form.

   a $x^2 + 6x + 4 = 0$ **b** $x^2 - 3x - \frac{1}{2} = 0$

   c $x(x - 5) = 9$ **d** $2x^2 = 2 - 7x$

4 Solve the equation

$$x^3 - 8x^2 + 15x = 0$$

Hint: Take out a common factor and use quadratic methods.

5 A function is given by the equation $f(x) = x^2 - 6x + 4$.

   a Complete the square on this function.

   b Hence, show that $f(x) \geqslant -5$ for all values of x.

Hint: If you square any number, the result is always greater than or equal to zero.

1 Solve these equations using the method of completing the square, leaving your answers in surd form.

a $x + \dfrac{23}{x} = 10$ **b** $x + 6 + \dfrac{2}{x} = 0$ **c** $\dfrac{2}{x} + \dfrac{1}{x+1} = 1$

Hint: In parts **a** and **b** multiply through by x to obtain a quadratic equation.

2 Complete the square on these functions and hence write the minimum value of each function.

a $f(x) = x^2 + 4x + 1$ **b** $f(x) = x^2 + 10x + 18$
c $f(x) = x^2 - 4x - 5$ **d** $f(x) = 2x^2 - 4x - 3$

3 For each of these quadratic graphs, find

   i the coordinates of the point where the graph cuts the y-axis

   ii the coordinates of the points where the graph cuts the x-axis

   iii the coordinates of the minimum (or maximum) point of each of the graphs.

   a $y = x^2 + 4x - 5$ **b** $y = x^2 - 6x + 9$
   c $y = 2x^2 - x - 3$ **d** $y = 3 - 2x - x^2$

4 Sketch each of the graphs in question **3**.

Hint: Be careful with part **d**. Notice that the x^2 term is negative. What does this tell you about the graph?

1 The sum of the reciprocals of two numbers that differ by 2 is $\frac{5}{12}$. Find the two numbers.

Hint: Write the sum of the reciprocals as an algebraic expression.

2 a Write $f(x) = 2x^2 - 16x + 9$ in the form $f(x) = a(x + b)^2 + c$ where a, b and c are to be determined.
  b Hence, give the minimum value of $f(x)$.
  c For what value of x does this occur?

3 Prove that $y = x^2 - 4x + 4$ is positive for all values of x.

4 a Sketch the graph of a circle centred at the origin with a radius of 3.
  b Sketch the graph of $y = 3(1 - x)$ on the same set of axes.
  c Hence, write the coordinates of one point of intersection of these graphs.
  d Use algebra to determine the other point of intersection.

1 Round each of the values in these calculations to 1 significant figure to produce an estimate. Then match the calculation with its actual answer.

Questions

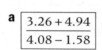

a $\dfrac{3.26 + 4.94}{4.08 - 1.58}$ **b** $\dfrac{4.84 \times 21}{3.5}$

c $\dfrac{2.5^3}{15.46 - 2.96}$

Answers

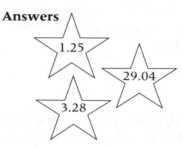

1.25
29.04
3.28

2 Sketch these quadratic graphs.

a $y = x^2 + 2x - 8$ **b** $y = x^2 - 2x - 3$

Hint: Find the coordinates of the points where each graph cuts the x and y axes. Complete the square and find the minimum point of each graph.

3 In triangle ABC, angle BAC = 84°, angle ABC = 52° and BC = 12 mm. Find the two missing sides of the triangle.

Hint: Find angle BCA and use the sine rule.

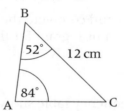

B
52°
12 cm
84°
A
C

4 A class of 30 students took a mental arithmetic test. Their percentage scores are shown.

78 35 65 58 77 74 69 70 41 55 79 78 80 85 90
62 59 56 52 63 71 70 76 82 88 92 43 79 86 51

a Construct a frequency table for these data.
b Construct a frequency polygon for these data.

1 The table gives information about the heights in centimetres of a group of 50 five-year-old girls.
Draw a histogram for these data.

Height, h, cm	Frequency
$95 < h \leqslant 100$	4
$100 < h \leqslant 105$	12
$105 < h \leqslant 110$	23
$110 < h \leqslant 115$	8
$115 < h \leqslant 120$	3

2 The table gives information about the time spent eating breakfast by a group of 100 people aged 20–34.

Time, t, min	Frequency	Class width	Frequency density
$0 < t \leqslant 5$	20	5	$20 \div 5 = 4$
$5 < t \leqslant 10$	38		
$10 < t \leqslant 30$	24		
$30 < t \leqslant 40$	10		
$40 < t \leqslant 60$	8		

a Copy and complete the table.
b Draw a histogram for the data.

3 The frequency table shows the time spent completing homework by a sample of students one Monday evening.

Time, t, hours	$0 < t \leqslant 0.5$	$0.5 < t \leqslant 1$	$1 < t \leqslant 2$	$2 < t \leqslant 2.5$	$2.5 < t \leqslant 3$
Frequency	56	32	32	10	6

a Complete a histogram for the data.
b How many students spent half an hour or less on their homework?
c How many students were in the sample?

1 This incomplete table and histogram give information about the length of 100 babies at birth.

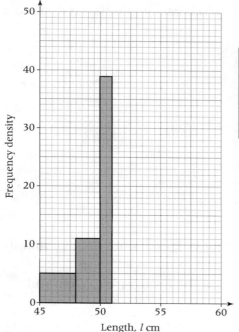

Length, l, cm	Frequency
$45 < l \leqslant 48$	
$48 < l \leqslant 50$	
$50 < l \leqslant 51$	
$51 < l \leqslant 54$	18
$54 < l \leqslant 56$	6

a Use the histogram to complete the table.
b Copy and complete the histogram.

2 Work out the height of the second bar in each of these histograms in terms of f.

a

Length, l, cm	Frequency	Bar height
$0 < l \leqslant 20$	16	4 cm
$20 < l \leqslant 60$	f	

b

Time, t, min	Frequency	Bar height
$0 < t \leqslant 15$	10	3 cm
$15 < t \leqslant 60$	f	

1 Hermione recorded the lengths, in minutes, of all the children's television programmes shown on terrestrial television during one weekday and displayed them in a histogram.

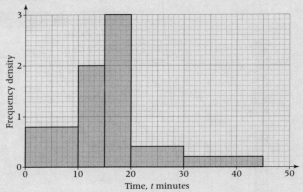

Time, *t* minutes

Ten children's programmes lasted more than 10 minutes but less than or equal to 15 minutes.

a Use the information in the histogram to copy and complete the table.

Time, *t*, min	$0 < t \leqslant 10$	$10 < t \leqslant 15$	$15 < t \leqslant 20$	$20 < t \leqslant 30$	$30 < t \leqslant 45$
Frequency		10			

Hermione repeated her task the next day and produced this table.

Time, *t*, min	Frequency	Height of bar
$0 < t \leqslant 20$	30	6 cm
$20 < t \leqslant 45$	f	

b Find the height of the second bar in this histogram in terms of f.

1 Find the value of these *without* using a calculator.
Show each step in your working clearly.

   a $49^{\frac{1}{2}}$ **b** $81^{\frac{1}{4}}$ **c** $27^{\frac{2}{3}}$ **d** $9^{\frac{3}{2}}$

   e $25^{\frac{5}{2}}$ **f** $100^{-\frac{1}{2}}$ **g** $32^{-\frac{3}{5}}$ **h** $0.008^{-\frac{2}{3}}$

2 Solve these pairs of simultaneous equations.

   a $x + y = 5$ **b** $4a + b = 7$ **c** $2p - 3q = 7$
      $3x - y = 11$ $3a + 2b = 4$ $5p - 2q = 1$

3 Find the angle marked x.

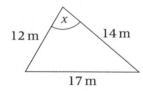

12 m   14 m   17 m

4 Isla and William are playing a computer game. They record
the time (in seconds) that it takes to complete each round
and compile the information shown in the table.

	Isla	Wiliam
Median	64	59
Lower quartile	50	44
Upper quartile	71	73
Minimum	45	40
Maximum	75	82

   a Draw box plots for each set of information on the same
axes.

   b Comment on and compare the performances of Isla and
William.

1 Change these measurements to the units given.

    a 720 mm to m   **b** 1500 cm^3 to litres

    c 35 000 cm to km   **d** 15 m^2 to cm^2

    e 92 cm^3 to mm^3 **f** 0.003 km^2 to m^2

    g 84 000 mm^3 to m^3 **h** 2 700 000 mm^2 to m^2

2 If a, b, c, r and h represent lengths, use dimension theory to deduce whether each of these expressions is a length, area, volume or none of these.

    a abc **b** $ab + rh$

    c $3a^2b$ **d** $2ah + 3r$

    e πabh **f** $\pi(r + h)$

    g $r(2ac - 4rh)$ **h** $\dfrac{a^2 + bc}{3}$

3 Find the area of triangle ABC.

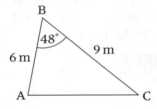

4 Find the area of an equilateral triangle with all sides of 7 cm.

5 The area of triangle PQR is 35 cm^2.
Find the angle PQR.

Hint: Rearrange the formula $A = \frac{1}{2}ab \sin C$.

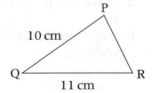

Solving problems using trigonometry

1 Calculate the area of these shaded segments.

a

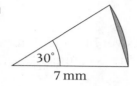

30°
7 mm

b

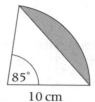

85°
10 cm

2 Marguerite wants to put 1001 sheep in her new field.
Each sheep must have 10 m² of land on which to graze.
By calculating the area of her field, work out whether
Marguerite has enough land on which to graze her sheep.

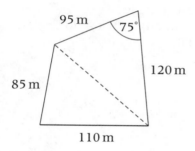

95 m
75°
120 m
85 m
110 m

Hint: Draw in the diagonal as shown and use the cosine rule to calculate
its length. Use this length and the cosine rule to find the angle opposite
75° in the quadrilateral. Use Area = ½ab sin C to find the area of each
triangle.

3 Find the volume of this frustrum.

Hint: Use similar triangles to find the
height of the complete cone. Then
calculate the volume of the small cone
and subtract from that of the larger cone.

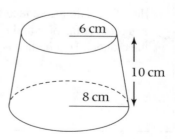

6 cm
10 cm
8 cm

1 Ben wrote down the volume of a sphere to be

$$V = 4\pi r^2$$

Jason was not sure of the correct answer but told Ben that he was wrong. How did Jason explain his comment?

2 A solid metal sphere of radius 3 cm is melted down to form a cone of base radius 3 cm. Work out the height of the cone.

3 a Calculate the area of triangle PQR.
  b T is a point on PQ such that angle PTR = 90°. Calculate the length of TR.

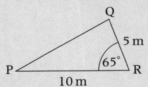

4 The curved surface area of a cylinder, radius r, is the same as the surface area of a sphere, radius $2r$. Show that the height of the cylinder is $8r$.

Hint: Calculate the surface area of the sphere, radius $2r$, leaving the answer in terms of π and r. Do the same for the curved surface area of the cylinder. Find h, the height of the cylinder.

1 Use your calculator to find the value of these, giving your answers to 4 significant figures.

a $\dfrac{3.241 \times 5.016}{2.897}$ **b** $\dfrac{9.194}{3.127 \times 1.563}$ **c** $\dfrac{1}{0.231} - \dfrac{8.254}{4.176}$

d $\sqrt{\left(\dfrac{2.564}{1.112}\right)}$ **e** $\dfrac{\sqrt{9.332} + (7.214)^3}{(8.246)^2}$

2 a Sketch the graph of the circle given by $x^2 + y^2 = 5$.
  b On the same set of axes, sketch the line $y = 3x - 1$.
  c Solve the pair of simultaneous equations

$$x^2 + y^2 = 5$$
$$y = 3x - 1$$

You may like to refer to your graph when giving your solutions.

3 Find the area of each triangle.

a
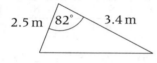
2.5 m 82° 3.4 m

b
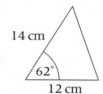
14 cm 62° 12 cm

4 This table shows the time taken in minutes by a group of 40 Mathematics teachers to solve a Sudoku puzzle.

Time, t	$0 \leqslant t < 5$	$5 \leqslant t < 10$	$10 \leqslant t < 15$	$15 \leqslant t < 20$	$20 \leqslant t < 25$
Frequency	2	6	12	7	3

Use this information to find

a the modal class
b the class containing the median time
c an estimate of the mean time.

1 a Copy and complete the table of values for the graph
$y = x^2 - 5x + 4$ for $-1 \leqslant x \leqslant 6$.

x	−1	0	1	2	3	4	5	6
x^2				4				
$-5x$				−10				
$+4$	4	4	4	4	4	4	4	4
y				−2				

b Hence, plot the graph of $y = x^2 - 5x + 4$ for $-1 \leqslant x \leqslant 6$.

c Use your curve to estimate the minimum point of
$y = x^2 - 5x + 4$.

2 a Copy and complete the table of values for the graph
$y = x^3 - 5x^2 + 2x + 8$ for $-2 \leqslant x \leqslant 5$.

x	−2	−1	0	1	2	3	4	5
x^3						27		
$-5x^2$						−45		
$+2x$						6		
$+8$	8	8	8	8	8	8	8	8
y						−4		

b Hence, plot the graph of $y = x^3 - 5x^2 + 2x + 8$ for $-2 \leqslant x \leqslant 5$.

c Use your curve to estimate the coordinates of the turning
points of the graph.

Hint: The turning points are where the graph changes from having a
positive gradient to a negative gradient or vice versa.

3 a Copy and complete the table of values for the graph
$f(x) = 6$ for $-6 \leqslant x \leqslant 6$.

x	−6	−5	−4	−3	−2	−1	0	1	2	3	4	5	6
$f(x)$											1.5		

b Hence plot the graph of $f(x) = \dfrac{6}{x}$.

c Use your graph to estimate the value of $f(3.5)$.

1 Use the diagram to solve these pairs of simultaneous equations.

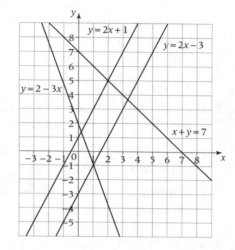

a $x + y = 7$
$\quad y = 2x + 1$

b $y = 2x - 3$
$\quad y = 2 - 3x$

c $y = 2x + 1$
$\quad y = 2 - 3x$

d Using the diagram, explain why $y = 2x + 1$ and $y = 2x - 3$ have no solutions.

2 Solve each pair of simultaneous equations in question **1** algebraically.

3 a Copy and complete this table to draw the graph of $y = 2x - x^2 + 3$.

x	−2	−1	0	1	2	3	4
$2x$	−4						
$-x^2$	−4						
$+3$	+3						
y	−5						

b Draw the graph of $y = 2x - x^2 + 3$.

c Use your graph to solve
i $2x - x^2 + 3 = 0$ and **ii** $2x - x^2 + 3 = 2$.

d By drawing an appropriate graph on the same set of axes, find approximate solutions to $2x - x^2 + 3 = \frac{1}{2}x + \frac{3}{2}$.

e By drawing an appropriate graph on the same set of axes, find approximate solutions to $x - x^2 + 4 = 0$.

1 By drawing appropriate graphs, find approximate solutions to the pair of simultaneous equations

$$x^2 + y^2 = 9$$
$$y = 2$$

2 **a** By drawing appropriate graphs, find approximate solutions to the pair of simultaneous equations

$$x^2 + y^2 = 25$$
$$y = 2x + 1$$

b Confirm these solutions by solving the simultaneous equations algebraically.

3 **a** Plot the graph of $y = 3^{x-1}$ for $-2 \leqslant x \leqslant 4$.
b Use your graph to find an approximate value for x when

   i $y = 2$ **ii** $y = 10$.

4 The graphs of $y = x^2 + x - 2$ and $y = kx$ are shown in the sketch.

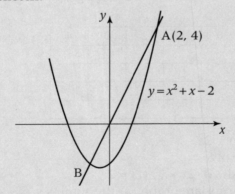

These graphs intersect at A and B.
A is the point (2, 4). Find B.

Hint: Find k by substituting the point (2, 4) into $y = kx$.
Use an algebraic method to find B.

1 Find the value of n that generates the term given from each of these sequences.

a $T_n = 5n - 3$; $T_n = 22$
b $T_n = (2n + 3)^2$; $T_n = 121$
c $T_n = \dfrac{n-1}{n+1}$; $T_n = \dfrac{99}{101}$
d $T_n = n^2 + 4n - 21$; $T_n = 75$

2 A function is given by the equation $f(x) = x^2 - 8x + 19$.

a Complete the square on this function.
b Hence, show that $f(x) \geqslant 3$ for all values of x.
c For what value of x does the minimum value of $f(x)$ occur?

3 Find the volume of this frustrum, giving your answer to 3 significant figures.

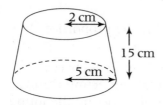

Hint: First, use similar triangles to find the height of the complete cone. Consider the problem as the difference in volume between a large and small cone.

4 Jason collected information about the time, in minutes, his classmates took to complete a Biology test.

Time, t, min	$0 \leqslant t < 20$	$20 \leqslant t < 30$	$30 \leqslant t < 35$	$35 \leqslant t < 60$
Frequency	4	8	10	8

Represent these data on a histogram.

Hint: Calculate the frequency density, i.e. divide the frequency by the class width. Plot the frequency density against time.

1 In a chocolate factory, a machine wraps 400 chocolate bars per minute.

   a Copy and complete the table to show the number of chocolate bars, b, wrapped for varying lengths of time, m (minutes).

m	1	2	3	4	5
b		800			

   b Sketch a graph of the relationship between b and m.
   c Write an algebraic relationship between b and m.
   Use this to find

   i the number of chocolate bars wrapped in 90 seconds
   ii the time taken to wrap 10 100 chocolate bars. Give your answer in minutes and seconds.

2 The cost, C, of carpeting a room is directly proportional to the area, a, of that room.

   a Given that the cost of 7.5 m^2 of carpet for Rebecca's bedroom is £168.75, find a formula connecting C and a.
   b Use your formula to find the cost of carpeting the lounge, which has an area of 14.5 m^2, in the same carpet.
   c The dining room costs £236.25 to cover in the same carpet. What is the area of the dining room?

3 P varies with the square of q. If $P = 51.2$ when $q = 3.2$

   a find a formula for P in terms of q
   b find the value of P when $q = 0.3$
   c find the value of q when $P = 16.2$.

4 Given that y is directly proportional to the cube root of x and that y is 12 when x is 8, find

   a a formula connecting y and x
   b the value of x when y is 24.

   Hint: Writing $\sqrt[3]{x}$ as $x^{\frac{1}{3}}$ is more usual in formulae.

1 A cleaning lady can clean a stately home in 18 hours.
The time taken, T, in hours to clean the stately home
is inversely proportional to the number of cleaning ladies, n,
that are employed.

  a Copy and complete the table to show the time taken, T, to
clean the stately home for varying numbers of cleaning
ladies, n.

n	1	2	3	4	5
T		9			

  b Sketch a graph of the relationship between T and n.
  c Write an algebraic relationship between T and n. Use this
    to find

    i the time taken when 8 cleaning ladies are employed
    ii the number of cleaning ladies needed to complete the
      cleaning in just half an hour.

2 A Mathematics department wants to buy new textbooks.
The amount, A, that the department can afford per textbook
is inversely proportional to the number of textbooks, n, that
they decide to buy.

  a Given that the department calculates that it can afford 30
    books at £14 each, find a formula connecting A and n.
  b What is the budget for this set of textbooks?
  c Use your formula to find the amount that they can afford
    to spend on each book if they wish to have 35 textbooks
    in this set.
  d The Mathematics department decide to buy *Fab Maths* at a
    cost of £10.50 per book. How many books can they buy?

3 y varies inversely with the square of x.
If $y = 12.8$ when $x = 5$,

  a find a formula for y in terms of x
  b find the value of y when $x = 2$
  c find the value of x when $y = 5$.

1 W is proportional to the square of z.
When $W = 39.2$, $z = 2.8$.

  a Write a formula for W in terms of z.
  b Calculate W when $z = 4.3$.
  c Calculate z when $W = 18.05$.

2 The time taken, T (hours), on a journey varies inversely as the average speed, s (km per hour), for the journey. When $T = 2.5$, $s = 48$.

  a Write a formula for T in terms of s.
  b Calculate the value of T when $s = 50$.

3 The graph shows the function $y = ab^x$.

  a Given that the graph passes through (1, 12) and (3, 192), find a and b.
  b Explain why the curve will pass through the point (4, 768).

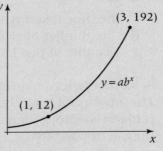

4 A scientist calculated that there were 14 million tonnes of herring in the North Sea in 1950. The decline of the population is modelled by the formula $P = xy^t$ as shown on the graph. In 1972, the scientist calculated that the population was now only 50 000 tonnes.

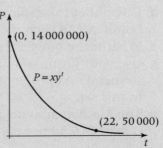

  a Find the values of x and y, giving your answers to 3 significant figures where appropriate.
  b Use your formula to estimate the size of the population in 1965. Give your answer to 2 significant figures.
  c Use your formula to estimate the year that the population became less than 5000 tonnes.

1 Work out these without using a calculator.

   a $(2.3 \times 10^4) \times (2 \times 10^6)$
   b $(3 \times 10^3) \times (3.5 \times 10^{-3})$
   c $(8.6 \times 10^5) \div (2 \times 10^8)$
   d $(1.8 \times 10^{-6}) \times (3 \times 10^{-2})$
   e $(1.5 \times 10^4)^2$

2 Solve these quadratic equations by factorising.

   a $x^2 + x - 12 = 0$ **b** $x^2 + 17x + 30 = 0$
   c $3x^2 - 23x - 8 = 0$ **d** $4x^2 - 1 = 0$

3 Solve these quadratic equations by completing the square.

   a $x^2 + 10x + 21 = 0$ **b** $x^2 + 6x = 0$
   c $x^2 - 8x + 1 = 0$ **d** $x^2 + 5x - 3 = 0$

4 Jamie's garden is twice as long as it is wide. The area of the garden is 162 m^2.

   a Write the area of the garden in square centimetres.
   b Calculate the length and width of the garden.
   c Jamie wants to construct a path to run along the diagonal of the garden. Calculate the length of this path.

5 Sarah gathered data on the number of minutes per day her colleagues spent on the Internet.

Minutes, m	$0 \leqslant m < 20$	$20 \leqslant m < 40$	$40 \leqslant m < 60$	$60 \leqslant m < 80$	$m \geqslant 80$
Frequency	8	15	12	5	0

Calculate an estimate for the mean number of minutes spent on the Internet.

1 Draw these vectors on square grid paper.

$$\mathbf{a} = \begin{pmatrix} -3 \\ 2 \end{pmatrix} \qquad \mathbf{b} = \begin{pmatrix} 6 \\ -4 \end{pmatrix} \qquad \mathbf{c} = \begin{pmatrix} -6 \\ -4 \end{pmatrix} \qquad \mathbf{d} = \begin{pmatrix} 2 \\ 3 \end{pmatrix}$$

a Write a pair of vectors that are parallel.
b Write a pair of vectors that are perpendicular.

2 Use Pythagoras' theorem to find the magnitude of each of the vectors in question **1**.

Hint: Magnitude is simply the length of the vector.

3 OABC is a parallelogram.
$\overrightarrow{OA} = \mathbf{a}$ and $\overrightarrow{OC} = \mathbf{c}$

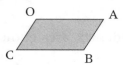

Find, in terms of **a** and **c**
a $\overrightarrow{BC}$ **b** $\overrightarrow{AB}$ **c** $\overrightarrow{AC}$

4 OAB is a triangle.
$\overrightarrow{OA} = \mathbf{a}$ and $\overrightarrow{OB} = \mathbf{b}$

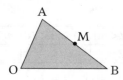

M is the midpoint of AB.
Find, in terms of **a** and **b**
a $\overrightarrow{AB}$ **b** $\overrightarrow{BA}$ **c** $\overrightarrow{AM}$

1 OABC is a trapezium.
OC and AB are parallel.
$AB = \frac{2}{3}OC$
$\overrightarrow{OA} = \mathbf{a}$ and $\overrightarrow{OC} = \mathbf{c}$
Find, in terms of $\mathbf{a}$ and $\mathbf{c}$

  a $\overrightarrow{AB}$ **b** $\overrightarrow{OB}$ **c** $\overrightarrow{CB}$

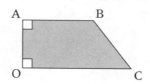

2 OPQR is a trapezium.
PQ and OR are parallel.
$PQ = 3OR$
$\overrightarrow{OP} = \mathbf{p}$ and $\overrightarrow{OR} = \mathbf{r}$
Find, in terms of $\mathbf{p}$ and $\mathbf{r}$

  a $\overrightarrow{PQ}$ **b** $\overrightarrow{OQ}$ **c** $\overrightarrow{QR}$

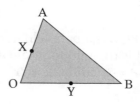

3 OAB is a triangle.
X is the midpoint of OA.
Y is the midpoint of OB.
$\overrightarrow{OA} = \mathbf{a}$ and $\overrightarrow{OB} = \mathbf{b}$
Find, in terms of $\mathbf{a}$ and $\mathbf{b}$

  a $\overrightarrow{AB}$ **b** $\overrightarrow{OX}$ **c** $\overrightarrow{XY}$

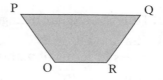

4 OXY is a triangle.
$XM : MY = 1 : 3$
$\overrightarrow{OX} = \mathbf{x}$ and $\overrightarrow{OY} = \mathbf{y}$
Find $\overrightarrow{OM}$ in terms of $\mathbf{x}$ and $\mathbf{y}$.

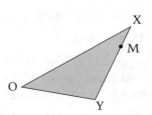

1 $\overrightarrow{OP} = \mathbf{p}$ and $\overrightarrow{OS} = \mathbf{s}$
$\overrightarrow{PQ} = \frac{1}{2}\mathbf{p}$ and $\overrightarrow{OR} = \frac{3}{2}\mathbf{s}$

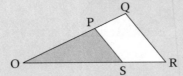

Prove that PS and QR are parallel.

2 ABCDEF is a regular hexagon with centre O.
$\overrightarrow{OA} = 2\mathbf{a}$ and $\overrightarrow{OB} = 2\mathbf{b}$

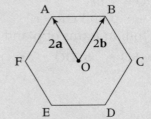

 a Express in terms of **a** and **b**
  i $\overrightarrow{AB}$ **ii** $\overrightarrow{BC}$

 b M is the midpoint of AF.
 Express $\overrightarrow{EM}$ in terms of **a**
 and **b**.

3 OPQR is a parallelogram.
M is the midpoint of OQ.
$\overrightarrow{OP} = 2\mathbf{p}$ and $\overrightarrow{OR} = 2\mathbf{r}$

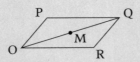

 a Express in terms of **p** and **r**
  i $\overrightarrow{PQ}$ **ii** $\overrightarrow{OM}$

 b Prove that P, M and R lie in a straight line.
 c What can you say about where M cuts PR?
 Refer to your working in part **b**.

Hint: For part **b** find $\overrightarrow{PM}$ and $\overrightarrow{MR}$.

1 a Expand and simplify $(p + q)^2$.

   b Hence, find the value of

$$2.84^2 + 2 \times 2.84 \times 1.16 + 1.16^2$$

2 a Copy and complete this table of values for the graph
$f(x) = 2 - \dfrac{1}{x}$.

x	-4	-3	-2	-1	$-\frac{1}{2}$	$-\frac{1}{4}$	0	$\frac{1}{4}$	$\frac{1}{2}$	1	2	3	4
$f(x)$						6					1.5		

   b Hence, plot the graph of $f(x) = 2 - \dfrac{1}{x}$.

   c Use your graph to estimate the value of $f(1.5)$.

3 Calculate the area of the shaded segment.

48° 5 cm

Hint: Find the area of the segment and use Area $= \frac{1}{2}ab \sin C$ to find the
area of the triangle.

4 Bob has two boxes of whiteboard pens.

Box number 1 contains 6 pens: 3 red, 2 blue and 1 black.
Box number 2 contains 12 pens: 5 red, 4 blue and 3 black.

Bob chooses one pen at random from each box. Calculate
the probability that the chosen pens are different colours.

1 An artist has a box of watercolour paints containing 4 pans of cadmium red colour and 6 pans of cobalt blue colour. In order to paint an abstract picture, the artist chooses a pan of colour at random from the box. He paints with this colour and then chooses a second pan of colour at random.

   a Copy and complete the tree diagram to show all possible outcomes.

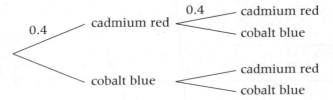

   b Find the probability that the artist chooses cobalt blue both times.

2 A tin contains 12 coloured pencils: 8 yellow and 4 green. A pencil is chosen at random from the tin, used to create a drawing and then replaced. A second pencil is then drawn from the tin at random.

   a Draw a tree diagram to show all possible outcomes.
   b Find the probability that the two pencils chosen are

     i both yellow   **ii** one of each colour.

   c Find the probability that at least one of the pencils chosen is green.

3 Bag A contains 7 white marbles and 3 black marbles.
Bag B contains 2 white marbles and 4 red marbles.
A marble is chosen at random from each bag.

   a Draw a tree diagram to show all possible outcomes.
   b Find the probability that the two marbles chosen are different colours.
   c Find the probability that at least one of the marbles chosen is red.

1 A box contains 10 chocolate biscuits and 5 plain biscuits. Iona chooses a biscuit at random and eats it. She then chooses a second biscuit at random and eats it.

   a Copy and complete the tree diagram to show all possible outcomes.

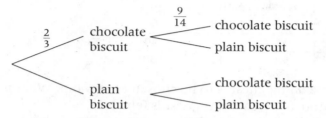

   b Find the probability that Iona chooses to eat

      i two plain biscuits   **ii** one of each type of biscuit.

   c Find the probability that at least one of the biscuits chosen is chocolate.

2 A teacher requires two classroom monitors to be in charge of the register. Two students are to be chosen at random from a class of 25 students: 15 boys and 10 girls.

   a Draw a tree diagram to show all possible outcomes.
   b Find the probability that the two students chosen are

      i both girls   **ii** a boy or a girl, in any order.

   c Find the probability that at least one of the students chosen is a boy.

3 The probability that Ava eats breakfast is 0.4. If Ava eats breakfast, the probability that she is late for school is 0.3. If Ava does not eat breakfast, the probability that she is late for school is 0.1.

   a Draw a tree diagram to show all possible outcomes.
   b Work out the probability that on any one day, Ava will *not* be late for school.

1 Wedding guests are given a choice of either 'Aberdeen Angus Fillet Steak with a whisky and cream sauce' or 'Roast Pave of Scottish Salmon with a mushroom sauce'. The table shows the choices of 100 guests.

	Steak	Salmon	Total
Male	42	18	60
Female	16	24	40
Total	58	42	100

  a One wedding guest is to be chosen at random. What is the probability that this guest is female?
  b One of the male guests is chosen at random. What is the probability that he chooses the Steak?
  c One of the guests who chose the Salmon is to be picked at random. What is the probability that they are female?

2 To start a game, a double-six must be obtained on the throw of two fair dice.

  a When any one fair dice is thrown, what is the probability of *not* obtaining a six?
  b Draw a tree diagram to show the two events 'six' and 'not six' for each of the two fair dice.
  c Calculate the probability of obtaining at least one six.
  d Calculate the probability of obtaining a double-six.

3 Isobel sits a multiple choice test with three questions. Each question has five possible answers. Isobel chooses the answer to each question at random. In order to pass the test, Isobel must correctly answer at least two of the three questions.

  a What is the probability that Isobel will correctly answer a question?
  b Draw a tree diagram to show all possible outcomes.
  c Find the probability that Isobel passes the test.

1 a Divide £350 in the ratio 3 : 4.
  b Divide £950 in the ratio 8 : 11.

2 If y is proportional to the square of x and when $x = 3$, $y = 27$, calculate
  a the value of y when $x = 4$
  b the value of x when $y = 75$.

3 Solve these simultaneous equations.

  a $x + y^2 = 22$ **b** $3x - y^2 = 5$ **c** $a^2 + b^2 = 20$
     $x = 6$ $x = 7$ $3a - b = 10$

4 OABC is a quadrilateral.
  X is the midpoint of AB.
  Y divides OC in the ratio 2 : 1.
  $\overrightarrow{OA} = \mathbf{a}$, $\overrightarrow{OB} = \mathbf{b}$ and $\overrightarrow{OC} = \mathbf{c}$

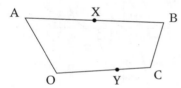

  Find

  a $\overrightarrow{AB}$ **b** $\overrightarrow{AX}$ **c** $\overrightarrow{OY}$ **d** $\overrightarrow{YX}$

5 A bag contains 4 red balls and 6 blue balls. Two balls are selected from the bag at random. If the first ball is not replaced before the second is selected, draw a tree diagram and use it to find

  a the probability of selecting two red balls
  b the probability of selecting a ball of each colour, in any order.

1 Write the equations of the three graphs labelled **i** to **iii**.

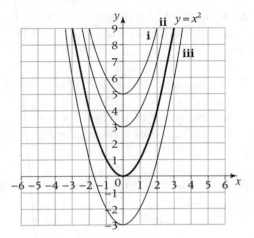

2 Write the equations of the three graphs labelled **i** to **iii**.

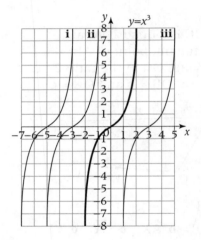

3 The graph of the function f(x) is shown.
What would the points A, B and C be translated to under the transformation

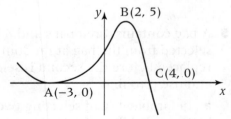

a f(x) + 2
b f(x) − 3
c f(x − 2)
d f(x + 3)?

1 Write the equations of the three graphs labelled **i** to **iii**.

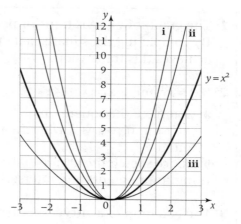

2 Write the equations of the three graphs labelled **i** to **iii**.

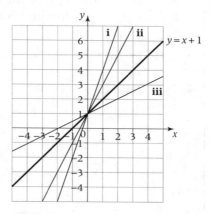

3 The graph of the function f(x) is shown. What would the points A, B and C be translated to under the transformation

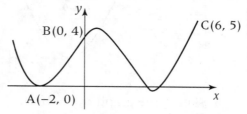

a $2f(x)$

b $\frac{1}{2}f(x)$

c $f(2x)$

d $f(\frac{1}{2}x)$?

1 The graph of $y = x^2$ is transformed to $y = x^2 + 6x + 7$. By completing the square, state the column vector that achieves this translation.

2 $f(x) = x^2$ and $g(x) = x^2 - 4x + 8$.

  a Complete the square on $g(x)$ and hence write $g(x)$ in the form $f(x - a) + b$ where a and b are constants to be found.

  b Hence sketch the graphs of $f(x)$ and $g(x)$, showing any minimum points and intersections with the axes.

3 The equation of a curve is $y = f(x)$ where $f(x) = x^2 - 6x + 14$.

  a Complete the square for $f(x)$.

  b Hence, sketch the graph of

    i $y = f(x)$

    ii $y = f(x + 3)$

4 The graph of $y = f(x)$ where $f(x) = \sin x$ for $0 \leqslant x \leqslant 360°$ is shown.

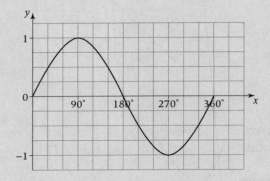

  a Sketch the graph of $y = 3f(x)$.

  b Sketch the graph of $y = f(2x)$.

  c Sketch the graph of $y = 2f(x) + 1$.

1 a varies in direct proportion to the square of b.
Copy and complete this table of values of a and b.

a	2	8	
b	2		5

2 a Copy and complete this table of values for the graph
$y = x^2 + 2x - 8$ for $-5 \leqslant x \leqslant 3$.

x	−5	−4	−3	−2	−1	0	1	2	3
x^2			9				1		
$2x$			−6				2		
−8	−8	−8	−8	−8	−8	−8	−8	−8	−8
y			−5				−5		

b Hence, plot the graph of $y = x^2 + 2x - 8$ for $-5 \leqslant x \leqslant 3$.
c Use your curve to find the minimum point of
$y = x^2 + 2x - 8$.

3 Use the cosine rule to find the missing side.

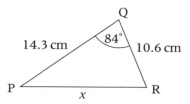

4 A bag contains 6 red and 4 blue marbles. A marble is chosen
at random from the bag, its colour is noted and then the
marble is replaced. A second marble is chosen at random.

a Draw a tree diagram to show all possible outcomes.
b Find the probability of choosing

   i two red marbles
   ii a marble of each colour, in any order.

1 We say that each of the sine and cosine graphs has a period of 360° because each graph repeats itself every 360°. Using sketch graphs to help you if necessary

  a for the sine graph, list five values of x for which $\sin x = 1$

  b for the cosine graph, list five values of x for which $\cos x = -1$.

2 Using graphs, find these ratios. Use a calculator to check the accuracy of your answers.

  a $\sin 30°$ **b** $\cos 30°$ **c** $\sin 210°$

  d $\cos 330°$ **e** $\sin 45°$ **f** $\cos 270°$

3 The first solution to each of these equations is given in brackets. Use a trigonometrical graph to find a second solution between 0° and 360°.

  a $\sin x = 0.5$ $(x = 30°)$ **b** $\sin x = \dfrac{1}{\sqrt{2}}$ $(x = 45°)$

  c $\cos x = 0.5$ $(x = 60°)$ **d** $\cos x = \dfrac{\sqrt{3}}{2}$ $(x = 30°)$

4 Using trigonometry, work out

  a $\sin 45°$ **b** $\cos 45°$ **c** $\tan 45°$

  Leave surds in your answers.

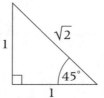

5 Use the sine rule to find a solution for θ.

  Use the sine graph to find a second solution. Sketch both solutions.

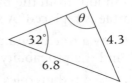

1 The tangent graph has a period of 180° because it repeats itself every 180°. Using a sketch graph to help you

   a list five values of x for which $\tan x = 0$

   b list five values of x where the graph of $y = \tan x$ has an asymptote.

2 Using graphs, find these ratios. Use a calculator to check the accuracy of your answers.

   a $\tan 30°$ **b** $\tan 45°$

   c $\tan 210°$ **d** $\tan 180°$

3 A missing angle θ is obtuse. Find θ if

   a $\sin \theta = 0.83$ **b** $\cos \theta = -0.41$

   c $\sin \theta = 0.75$ **d** $\tan \theta = -0.32$

4 Copy and complete this table, using your calculator and question **4** in HW2 to help you.

	0°	30°	45°	60°	90°
sin				$\dfrac{\sqrt{3}}{2}$	
cos		$\dfrac{\sqrt{3}}{2}$			
tan		$\dfrac{1}{\sqrt{3}}$		$\sqrt{3}$	

5 Solve these equations for angles from 0° to 360°.

   a $\sin x = 0.362$ **b** $\cos x = 0.866$ **c** $\tan x = 0.577$

   d $\cos x = -0.289$ **e** $\tan x = 0.412$ **f** $\sin x = -0.707$

1 The graph of $y = g(x)$ where $g(x) = \cos x$ for $0 \leqslant x \leqslant 360°$ is shown.

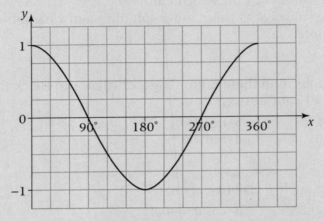

a Sketch the graph of $y = \cos 2x$ for $0 \leqslant x \leqslant 360°$.
b Sketch the graph of $y = \cos(x - 90)$ for $0 \leqslant x \leqslant 360°$.

2 a Use your calculator to find the first solution to the equation

$$\cos x = 0.354$$

b By considering the graph of $y = \cos x$, find a second solution for x such that $0 \leqslant x \leqslant 360°$.

3 Find the solution to the equation

$$\sin x = 0.584$$

if it is known that the angle x is obtuse.

N1 HW1

1 a $\frac{11}{12}$ b $\frac{17}{45}$ c $1\frac{1}{2}$ d $1\frac{2}{3}$

2 a $\frac{534}{999}$ b $\frac{1}{15}$ c $2\frac{24}{99}$ d $-1\frac{98}{99}$

3 a $x = 10$ b $x = -1$ c $x = 3$
 d $x = -3$ e $x = 18$ f $x = 4$

4 a 0.45 b 25

S1 HW1

1 a $720 = 2 \times 2 \times 2 \times 2 \times 3 \times 3 \times 5$
 b $84 = 2 \times 2 \times 3 \times 7$
 c $910 = 2 \times 5 \times 7 \times 13$
 d $36 = 2 \times 2 \times 3 \times 3$
 e $256 = 2 \times 2 \times 2 \times 2 \times 2 \times 2 \times 2 \times 2$

2 ai 12 aii 252
 bi 16 bii 11 520
 ci 14 cii 5460
 di 1 dii 16 380
 e Co-prime

3 a 2.056×10^3 b 8.71342×10^5
 c 4.86×10^{-4} d 2.58×10^5
 e 3.6×10^{-4}

4 a 3×10^6 b 2.1×10^6
 c 4×10^{16} d 3.6×10^{11}
 e 8×10^1

5 a Circumference = 52.8 cm (3 s.f.)
   Area = 55.4 cm² (3 s.f.)
 b Circumference = 18.2 cm (3 s.f.)
   Area = 26.4 cm² (3 s.f.)

A1 HW1

1 a 3.2×10^2 b 4×10^{10}
 c 8×10^{-9} d 5×10^{18}

2 a $240 = 2 \times 2 \times 2 \times 2 \times 3 \times 5$
   $504 = 2 \times 2 \times 2 \times 3 \times 3 \times 7$
 b 24

3 a 62.8 cm² (3 s.f.)
 b 251.3 cm³ (1 d.p.)

4 a 2997.1 mm² (1 d.p.)
 b 18.1 m² (3 s.f.)

N2 HW1

1 a 3.8×10^6 b 260 000
 c 6.84% (3 s.f.)

2 a $15 - 20x$ b $12a^2 + 18ab$
 c $y^3 + y^2x$ d $x^2 + 10x + 21$
 e $2t^2 + 7t - 15$ f $p^2 + 9p + 43$

3 a 75 cm³

4 a $x = 138°$ b $a = 93°$ $b = 35°$

A2 HW1

1 a Smaller b Larger c Smaller
 d Larger

2 a 4.33 b 3.8 c 0.216
 d 0.002 e 10 200 f 1.200
 g 2.00 h 45 000

3 a $2a(2b - 1)$ b $5x(2x - 3)$
 c $a^2c(ab^2 + 3)$ d $p(3p + 9p^2 + q)$
 e $(a - 5)(x + y)$ f $(x + 3)(x + 5)$
 g $(x + 6)(x - 1)$ h $(3x + 2)(x - 4)$

4 226 cm³

5 151 cm²

D1 HW1

1 ai 36 aii 36
 aiii 45 aiv 72
 bi 76% bii 85%
 biii 63.5% biv 57.5%

2 a $x = 6$ b $a = 8$ c $t = 2$
 d $p = 1.5$ e $y = 2$ f $m = 5$

3 a 8.48 cm² (3 s.f.)
 b $x = 159.5°$ (1 d.p.)

4 62.4 cm² (1 d.p.)

N3 HW1

1 a £21 b £14 c £6.30
 d £2.45 e £4.38 f £1.14

2 a $x = 2$ b $x = -1$

3 3.71 cm (3 s.f.)

4 Mean is 79.77, so claim is correct.

S2 HW1

1 a UB = 12.035025 m²
   LB = 11.965025 m²
 b UB = 11° LB = 9°
 c UB = 7.53 g/cm³ (3 s.f.)
   LB = 7.47 g/cm³ (3 s.f.)

2 a $x > 11$ **b** $x \leqslant -3$ **c** $n \geqslant -4$
  d $x \geqslant -3$ **e** $x \geqslant 35$ **f** $x < 9$
  g $3 < x < 4$ **h** $-8 \leqslant x \leqslant 8$
3 1230 mm^3 (3 s.f.)
4

Year group	7	8	9	10	11
No. of pupils	10	10	10	11	9

A3 HW1

1 Option 2
2 32
3 a $x = -16$ **b** $x = 10$
4 $x = 63°$ $y = 27°$
5 a May not use a gym as they play hockey; may use a gym more as they like sport; excluding all people not in this hockey club
  b How many times a month do you visit a gym?
   None 1–4 5–8 9–12
   More than 12

D2 HW1

1 a 0.05, 11%, 16%, $\frac{2}{9}$, 0.23, 25%, $\frac{4}{7}$, $\frac{11}{16}$
  b 0.03, $\frac{1}{13}$, 18%, $\frac{4}{15}$, 28%, 0.4, 0.75, $\frac{4}{5}$
2 a $x = -0.394$ or -7.61
  b $a = 2.15$ or -0.155
  c $t = 2.28$ or 0.219
  d $t = 1.39$ or 0.360
3 a $x = 144°$ (D and B are opposite angles of a cyclic quadrilateral)
  b $y = 72°$ (Angle at centre is twice the angle subtended at the circumference)
4 a 3 **b** 1

A4 HW1

1 a $150 = 2 \times 3 \times 5 \times 5$
   $735 = 3 \times 5 \times 7 \times 7$
  bi 15 **bii** 7350

2 a 3, 5, 9, 17, 33; Divergent
  b $\frac{1}{2}, \frac{1}{6}, \frac{1}{12}, \frac{1}{20}, \frac{1}{30}$; Converges to limiting value of 0
  c 6, 12, 20, 30, 42; Divergent
  d 9, 8, 7, 6, 5; Divergent
  e 4, −2, 4, −2, 4; Oscillates between 4 and −2
3 a $(x-3)(x+3)$ **b** $(p-7)(p+7)$
  c $(2n-9)(2n+9)$ **d** $(x - \frac{2}{5})(x + \frac{2}{5})$
  e $3a(a-2)(a+2)$
4 20.6 cm^2 (3 s.f.)
5 $\frac{14g + 10b}{30}$

D3 HW1

1 a $3\frac{1}{3}$ **b** $1\frac{7}{8}$ **c** 19 **d** $1\frac{1}{2}$
2 ai $(1, 7)$ **aii** $(5, -2)$ **aiii** $(\frac{3}{8}, -3)$
  b $(\frac{3}{2}, \frac{5}{2})$
3 BDA = BCA = 90°, AB = BC (isosceles), AD = DC (perpendicular cuts isosceles in half at base), therefore triangles are congruent by SAS.
4 Systematic, say, every 10th cake bar starting at cake 2 is sampled.

N4 HW1

1 $\frac{3}{9}$, 0.6, 60%; $\frac{1}{25}$, 0.04, 4%; $\frac{9}{20}$, 0.45, 45%; $\frac{3}{16}$, 0.1875, 18.75%; $\frac{7}{8}$, 0.875, 87.5%
2 a

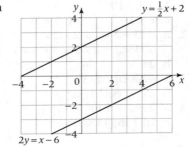

  b $y = \frac{1}{2}x + 2$

3 75.4 cm^2 (3 s.f.)

4 a

	1	2	3	4	5	6
1	2	3	4	5	6	7
2	3	4	5	6	7	8
3	4	5	6	7	8	9
4	5	6	7	8	9	10
5	6	7	8	9	10	11
6	7	8	9	10	11	12

4 b $\frac{1}{9}$

S3 HW1

1 a £12 800   **b** 28.4% (3 s.f.)
  c 12 years
2 a Parallel   **b** Parallel
  c Perpendicular **d** Perpendicular
  e Parallel
3 46 cm (3 s.f.)
4 a Add option boxes, for example
  I don't go on holiday ☐
  1–2 times ☐   3–4 times ☐
  5 times or more ☐
  b On which continent do you
  prefer to holiday?

N5 HW1

1 a $\frac{1}{30}$ **bi** 6 **bii** 14
2 a $\frac{3}{x-5}$ **b** $\frac{x-2}{3(x-9)}$
3 93.75 cm^3
4 a Week 1: $\frac{3}{5}$ Week 2: $\frac{23}{40}$
    Week 3: $\frac{19}{30}$ Week 4: $\frac{3}{5}$
    Week 5: $\frac{3}{5}$ **b** $\frac{3}{5}$

A5 HW1

1 Angela has £3000, Ayesha has £500
2 a $y = 3x + 1$ **b** $y = 3 - 2x$
  c $y = \frac{x}{3} + 2$
3 A and C, B and D, E and F
4 a

	Mashing	Chipping	Roasting	Total
Female	16	12	12	40
Male	12	28	20	60
Total	28	40	32	100

  bi $\frac{8}{25}$ **bii** $\frac{3}{25}$ **c** 60

S4 HW1

1 a £68   **b** £54.40   **c** 36%
2 a $3n + 1$ **b** $5n - 3$ **c** $(n + 1)^2$
  d $n^2 - n + 3$
3 a $a = 63°$ **b** $b = 115°$ $c = 68°$
4 a $\frac{37}{45}$
  b $\frac{8}{45}$ The assumption made is that
    the events are mutually
    exclusive

N6 HW1

1 a $k = 8.96$ **b** Density
  c 1900.0 g (1 d.p.)   **d** 325 cm^3
2 $x = 3$, and so dimensions are 16 cm
  and 6 cm
3 a 7.30 cm (3 s.f.)
  b 17.3 mm (3 s.f.)
4 ai 38   **aii** 50
  b

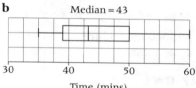

Median = 43

Time (mins)

A6 HW1

1 $n = \frac{2}{3}$
2

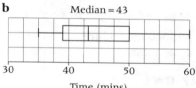

$y = x - 1$

$y = 5 - x$

3 a $a = 4.84$ (3 s.f.)
  b $x = 54.2°$ (3 s.f.)
  c $b = 22.0$ (3 s.f.)
  d $y = 28.1°$ (3 s.f.)
4 a $\frac{13}{20}$ **b** Mutually exclusive

D4 HW1

1 **a** 5^9 **b** 4^4 **c** x^{14} **d** 2^2
  e a^8 **f** y^{-2}

2 **a** $ab = 40$ and $2a + 2b = 26$
  b $a = 8$ cm, $b = 5$ cm

3 **a** A′ = (3, 0) B′ = (3, 9) C′ = (9, 0)
  b A″ = (−1, 4) B″ = (−1, 1)
    C″ = (−3, 4)

4 $\frac{8}{15}$

S5 HW1

1 **a** $\frac{\sqrt{3}}{3}$ **b** $\frac{\sqrt{5}}{5}$ **c** $3\frac{\sqrt{7}}{7}$ **d** $2\sqrt{5}$
  e $5\sqrt{2}$ **f** $\frac{\sqrt{3}}{6}$

2 **a** $x = \frac{y-8}{3}$ **b** $t = \frac{3s+r}{2}$
  c $q = \frac{s+r}{p}$ **d** $c = \frac{b}{a}$
  e $q = 2p - t$ **f** $a = \frac{xy}{b-c}$
  g $q = \frac{ab-pr}{p-a}$ **h** $x = \frac{cab}{ca-1}$

3 5000 ml = 5 litres

4 22 mins

A7 HW1

1 **a** $x = c - ab$ **b** $x = \frac{r+q}{p^3}$
  c $x = c(f - d)$ **d** $x = 16 - k$
  e $x^2 = m^2 - n^2$

2 **a** $x = \frac{b-q}{p-a}$ **b** $x = \frac{km}{k-t}$
  c $x = \frac{p(A-1)}{A+1}$ **d** $x = \frac{p}{m-n+1}$

3 **a** 15 cm **b** 28.1° (3 s.f.)

4 **a, b**

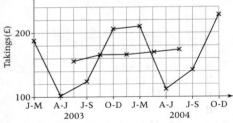

  b 154.75, 160.25, 162.75, 167.25,
  173
  c Suggests takings are increasing

D5 HW1

1 **a** 3.28 **b** 29.04 **c** 1.25

2 **a**

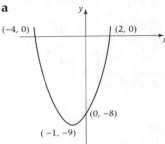

  b

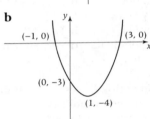

3 AC = 9.51 cm and AB = 8.38 cm
  (3 s.f.)

4 **a**

Scores	Frequency
$30 < s \leqslant 40$	1
$40 < s \leqslant 50$	2
$50 < s \leqslant 60$	6
$60 < s \leqslant 70$	6
$70 < s \leqslant 80$	9
$80 < s \leqslant 90$	5
$90 < s \leqslant 100$	1

  b

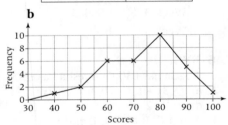

S6 HW1

1 **a** 7 **b** 3 **c** 9 **d** 27
  e 3125 **f** $\frac{1}{10}$ **g** $\frac{1}{8}$ **h** 25

2 a $x = 4$, $y = 1$ **b** $a = 2$, $b = -1$
c $p = -1$, $q = -3$
3 $81.3°$ (3 s.f.)
4 a

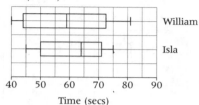

William

Isla

Time (secs)

b Isla's median time is faster than William's. William achieved the fastest (shortest) time for completing a round, but was more erratic.

A8 HW1

1 a 5.612 **b** 1.881 **c** 2.352
d 1.518 **e** 5.566
2 a, b

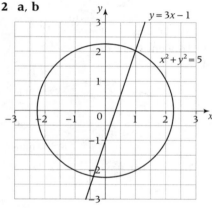

$y = 3x - 1$

$x^2 + y^2 = 5$

c $x = 1$, $y = 2$ and $x = -\frac{2}{5}$, $y = -2\frac{1}{5}$
3 a 4.2 m^2 (1 d.p.)
b 74.2 m^2 (1 d.p.)
4 a $10 \leqslant t < 15$ **b** $10 \leqslant t < 15$
c 9.75 mins

A9 HW1

1 a $n = 5$ **b** $n = 4$
c $n = 100$ **d** $n = 8$

2 a $f(x) = (x - 4)^2 + 3$
b $(x - 4)^2 \geqslant 0$, which implies
$(x - 4)^2 + 3 \geqslant 3$
c $x = 4$
3 612.6 cm^3
4

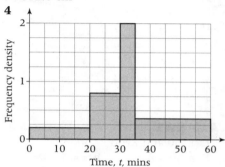

Frequency density

Time, t, mins

S7 HW1

1 a 4.6×10^{10} **b** 1.05×10^{1}
c 4.3×10^{-3}
d 5.4×10^{-8} **e** 2.25×10^{8}
2 a $x = 3$ or -4 **b** $x = -2$ or -15
c $x = 8$ or $-\frac{1}{3}$ **d** $x = \frac{1}{2}$ or $-\frac{1}{2}$
3 a $x = -3$ or -7 **b** $x = 0$ or -6
c $x = 4 + \sqrt{15}$ or $4 - \sqrt{15}$
d $x = -\frac{5}{2} + \frac{\sqrt{37}}{4}$ or $-\frac{5}{2} - \frac{\sqrt{37}}{4}$
4 a $1\,620\,000 \text{ cm}^2$
b Length = 18 m, width = 9 m
c 20.1 m (3 s.f.)
5 37 mins

D6 HW1

1 a $p^2 + 2pq + q^2$ **b** 16
2 a $f(x) = 2 - \frac{1}{x}$

x	-4	-3	-2	-1	$-\frac{1}{2}$	$-\frac{1}{4}$	0	$\frac{1}{4}$	$\frac{1}{2}$	1	2	3	4
$f(x)$	$2\frac{1}{4}$	$2\frac{1}{3}$	$2\frac{1}{2}$	3	4	6	$-$	-2	0	1	$1\frac{1}{2}$	$1\frac{2}{3}$	$1\frac{3}{4}$

b

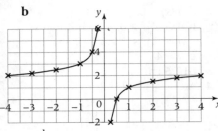

c $1\frac{1}{3}$

3 1.18 cm^2 (3 s.f.)

4 $\frac{23}{36}$

A10 HW1

1 £150 and £200

2 a $y = 48$ **b** $x = 5$

3 a $y = 4$ or -4 **b** $y = 4$ or -4
   c $a = 4$, $b = 2$ and $a = 2$, $b = -4$

4 a $\mathbf{b} - \mathbf{a}$ **b** $\frac{1}{2}(\mathbf{b} - \mathbf{a})$
   c $\frac{2}{3}\mathbf{c}$ **d** $\frac{1}{2}(\mathbf{a} + \mathbf{b}) - \frac{2}{3}\mathbf{c}$

5 a $\frac{2}{15}$ **b** $\frac{8}{15}$

S8 HW1

1

a	2	8	12.5
b	2	4	5

2 a $y = x^2 + 2x - 8$

x	-5	-4	-3	-2	-1	0	1	2	3
x^2	25	16	9	4	1	0	1	4	9
$2x$	-10	-8	-6	-4	-2	0	2	4	6
-8	-8	-8	-8	-8	-8	-8	-8	-8	-8
y	7	0	-5	-8	-9	-8	-5	0	7

b

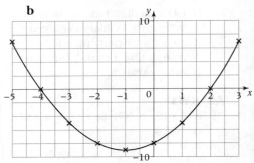

c $(-1, -9)$

3 16.9 cm (3 s.f.)

4 a

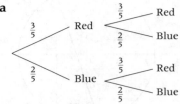

   bi $\frac{9}{25}$ **bii** $\frac{12}{25}$